Hey, Andrew! Teach Me Some Greek!

A BIBLICAL GREEK WORKTEXT

LEVEL 2
ANSWER KEY

BY KAREN MOHS

Dear Parent/Teacher:

This answer key is designed to assist you in teaching Greek Workbook Level Two.

The Level Two workbook will familiarize your student with Greek words. Six nouns, four verbs, and a conjunction are introduced, which form the basis for grammatical concepts to be learned in Level Three.

As with Level One, please note the "More Practice" pages (directly following the introduction of each new word). These pages are beneficial in firmly planting the new item into the student's memory. It is best if they are completed. Occasionally, however, too much repetition can cool a student's enthusiasm. For some, half a page of practice will be adequate. You are the best judge of your student's needs and abilities.

Daily flashcard practice is essential. Please do not neglect this effective learning tool. The letters and words for flashcard use are located at the end of the workbook.

Glossaries at the end of the workbook include definitions of the Greek words used in the word recognition exercises.

In addition to this answer key, quizzes/exams and flashcards on a ring are available. The audio pronunciation CD or cassette tape includes Greek letters, vocabulary, "The Greek Alphabet Song," and a reading of *The Reader*.

Most importantly, continue to make this an enjoyable learning experience and a happy memory for both you and your student.

References:
New Testament Greek For Beginners by J. Gresham Machen
Essentials of New Testament Greek by Ray Summers
A Short Syntax of New Testament Greek by H.P.V. Nunn
Moods and Tenses of New Testament Greek by Earnest De Witt Burton
A Manual Grammar of the Greek New Testament by Dana and Mantey
Exhaustive Concordance of the Bible by James Strong

ISBN-13: 978-1-931842-07-5
ISBN-10: 1-931842-07-8

Greek 'n' Stuff
P.O. Box 882
Moline, IL 61266-0882
www.greeknstuff.com

Revised 2/05

SCHEDULE OF LESSONS
(PROPOSAL FOR LEVEL TWO)

In overview, the *Hey, Andrew! Teach Me Some Greek!* workbooks are designed such that the student ideally completes one page per day (and practices his or her flashcards each day as well). (It should be noted that older students often complete more than one page per day when they are working in the early levels.) The workbooks were not designed within a framework of "lessons." Many parents have told us they appreciate this approach. It is easy to follow, without need of additional parent/teacher preparation and scheduling.

However, some parents/teachers prefer the "lesson" approach. Please be aware that this "Schedule of Lessons" is an artificial grid placed over a series not written with this grid in mind. The assigned pages are arbitrary and should be modified so the student can progress through the workbooks at a pace suitable to his or her age/skill level.

A note about our methodology:
This series begins gently and advances gradually, providing plenty of reinforcement through a wide variety of workbook activities and translation exercises. By introducing new concepts slowly, *Hey, Andrew! Teach Me Some Greek!* avoids the pitfall common to many foreign language courses whereby the student suddenly faces a steep learning curve, becomes frustrated, fails to internalize the language, and develops an aversion to foreign language study in general. The overwhelming response from those using *Hey, Andrew! Teach Me Some Greek!* can be summed up by the words we hear so often: "This is my student's favorite subject."

Lesson 1
Pages 1-6 - Alphabet review - Part 1

Teacher tip:
For more information on the alphabet, see Lesson 1 of *New Testament Greek for Beginners* by J. Gresham Machen or pages 7-12 of *Basics of Biblical Greek* by William D. Mounce.

Lesson 2
Pages 7-12 - Alphabet review - Part 2

Lesson 3
Pages 13-18 - Alphabet review - Part 3

Lesson 4
Pages 19-24 - Alphabet review - Part 4

Lesson 5

Pages 25-28 - Alphabet practice

Lesson 6

Pages 29-32 - Alphabet practice

Lesson 7

Pages 33-36 - Alphabet practice

****
QUIZ #1 (optional)
****

Lesson 8

Pages 37-39 - New vocabulary - ἄνθρωπος, vocabulary practice

~~~~~~

Teacher tip:

Your student should write the accents and breathing marks (the little symbols above the letters) along with writing the words. This practice will aid in learning these marks along with the spelling of the words. (Certain Greek words with entirely distinct meanings would look identical without the accents/breathing marks. For example, ἕν means *one*, but ἐν means *in*.)

It is best, when learning Greek, to think of the words along with the accents/breathing marks as one unit rather than as separate parts. As you will learn later, the accents can change form and change position on a particular word as the word endings change. Especially in nouns, it is essential to know where the accent *starts* (that is, where the accent is located on the dictionary form of the word).

~~~~~~

> *English derivatives:*
> ἄνθρωπος (anthropology, philanthropy, anthropic, misanthrope,
> theanthropic, pithecanthropus, sinanthropus, anthroposophy,
> anthropopathism, anthropophagus, lycanthrope)

Lesson 9

Pages 40-42 - Vocabulary practice - Part 1

Lesson 10

Pages 43-47 - New vocabulary - ἀδελφός, vocabulary practice

> *English derivatives:*
> ἀδελφός (Philadelphia)

Lesson 11

Pages 48-52 - Vocabulary practice - Part 2

Lesson 12
 Pages 53-57 - New vocabulary - ἀπόστολος, vocabulary practice

> *English derivatives:*
> ἀπόστολος (apostle, apostlehood, apostleship)

Lesson 13
 Pages 58-62 - Vocabulary practice - Part 3

Lesson 14
 Pages 63-67 - New vocabulary - βλέπω, vocabulary practice

Lesson 15
 Pages 68-72 - Vocabulary practice - Part 4

****
QUIZ #2 (optional)
****

****
MIDTERM EXAM (optional)
****

Lesson 16
 Pages 73-77 - New vocabulary - γινώσκω, vocabulary practice

> *English derivatives:*
> γινώσκω (diagnosis, prognosis, gnostic, gnosis, agnosia, gnomon, gnome)

Lesson 17
 Pages 78-82 - Vocabulary practice - Part 5

Lesson 18
 Pages 83-87 - New vocabulary - καί, vocabulary practice

Lesson 19
 Pages 88-92 - Vocabulary practice - Part 6

Lesson 20
 Pages 93-97 - New vocabulary - δοῦλος, vocabulary practice

> *English derivatives:*
> δοῦλος (hierodule, hierodulic)

Lesson 21
 Pages 98-102 - Vocabulary practice - Part 7

Lesson 22
   Pages 103-107 - New vocabulary - λόγος, vocabulary practice

> *English derivatives:*
>   λόγος (words ending in -logy [such as biology, doxology, etc.],
>   logo, logic, logistic, apology, analogous, monologue, prologue,
>   epilogue, anthology, philology, tautology, logarithm, syllogism,
>   homologous, heterologous, Decalogue, paralogism, apologue,
>   logogriph, logomachy, brachylogy, bradylogia)

Lesson 23
   Pages 108-112 - Vocabulary practice - Part 8

****
QUIZ #3 (optional)
****

Lesson 24
   Pages 113-117 - New vocabulary - γράφω, vocabulary practice

> *English derivatives:*
>   γράφω (words ending in -graph [such as paragraph, autograph, etc.],
>   words ending in -graphy [such as photography, oceanography,
>   etc.], graphic, program, diagram, graphite, epigram,
>   pseudepigrapha, agraphia, agrapha, Hagiographa, paleography,
>   graptolite)

Lesson 25
   Pages 118-122 - Vocabulary practice - Part 9

Lesson 26
   Pages 123-127 - New vocabulary - υἱός, vocabulary practice

Lesson 27
   Pages 128-132 - Vocabulary practice - Part 10

Lesson 28
   Pages 133-137 - New vocabulary - διδάσκω, vocabulary practice

> *English derivatives:*
>   διδάσκω (didactic, didactically, didacticism)

Lesson 29
   Pages 138-142 - Vocabulary practice - Part 11

Lesson 30
   Page 143 - Final review

****
QUIZ #4 (optional)
****

****
FINAL EXAM (optional)
****

Appendix

Glossaries 145

Greek Alphabet 147

Vowels and Diphthongs 147

Flashcard Tips 148

LET'S REVIEW THE GREEK ALPHABET

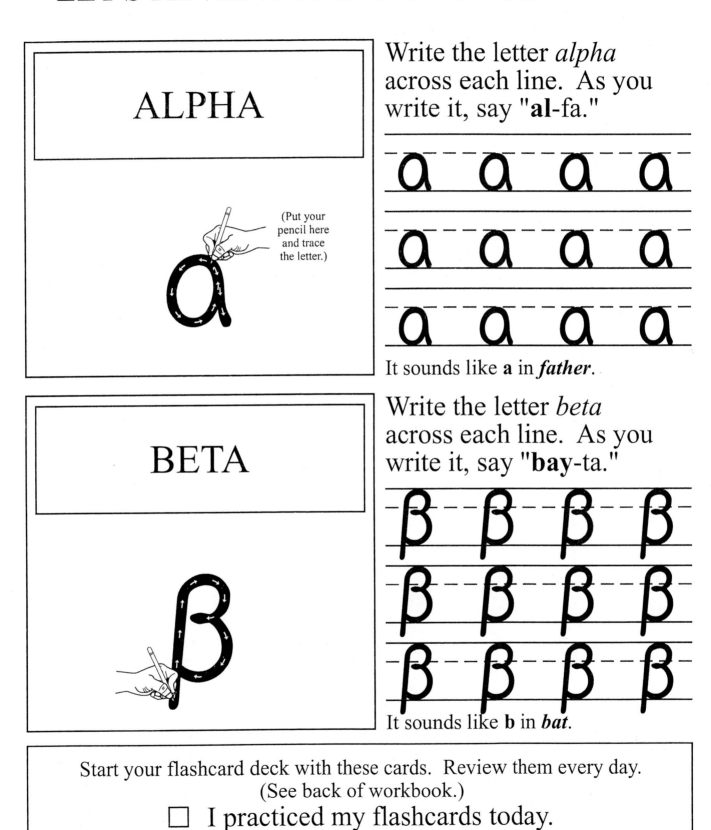

ALPHA

(Put your pencil here and trace the letter.)

Write the letter *alpha* across each line. As you write it, say **"al**-fa."

α α α α

α α α α

α α α α

It sounds like **a** in *father*.

BETA

Write the letter *beta* across each line. As you write it, say **"bay**-ta."

β β β β

β β β β

β β β β

It sounds like **b** in *bat*.

Start your flashcard deck with these cards. Review them every day.
(See back of workbook.)
☐ I practiced my flashcards today.

LET'S PRACTICE

Write the first two Greek alphabet letters in order.

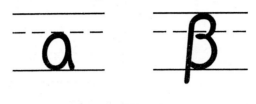

Write the names of the Greek letters.

α   <u>alpha</u>

β   <u>beta</u>

Draw lines from the Greek letters to their sounds.

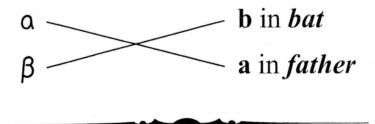

Color the correct letters blue.

alpha	α	β	β	α	β	β	α	β	α
beta	α	α	β	β	α	α	β	β	α

☐ I practiced my flashcards today.

MORE ALPHABET REVIEW

GAMMA

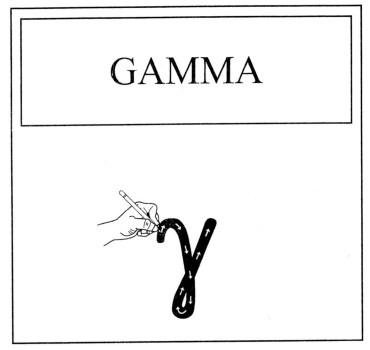

Write the letter *gamma* across each line. As you write it, say "**gam**-ma."

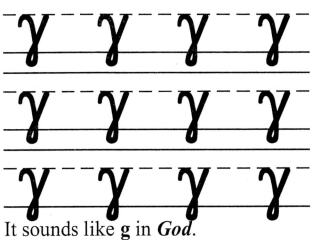

It sounds like **g** in *God*.

DELTA

Write the letter *delta* across each line. As you write it, say "**del**-ta."

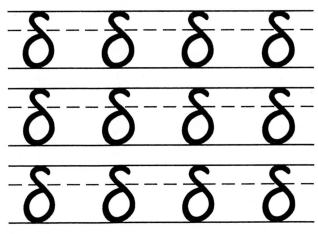

It sounds like **d** in *dog*.

☐ I practiced my flashcards today. (Add the new cards.)

LET'S PRACTICE

Write the first four Greek alphabet letters in order.

Circle the correct names of the Greek letters.

alpha beta δ gamma (delta)	alpha (beta) β gamma delta	alpha beta γ (gamma) delta
(alpha) beta α gamma delta	alpha beta γ (gamma) delta	alpha beta δ gamma (delta)

Write the Greek letters on the lines beside their names.

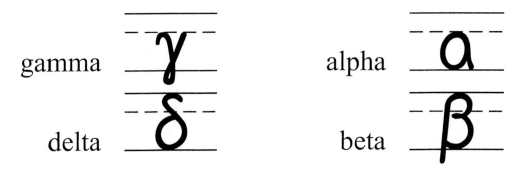

gamma γ   alpha α

delta δ   beta β

☐ I practiced my flashcards today.

MORE ALPHABET REVIEW

EPSILON

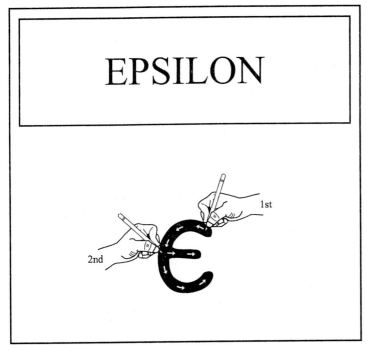

Write the letter *epsilon* across each line. As you write it, say "**ep**-si-lon."

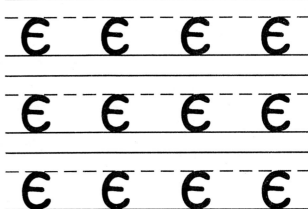

It sounds like **e** in *get*.

ZETA

Write the letter *zeta* across each line. As you write it, say "**zay**-ta."

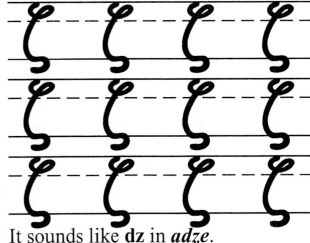

It sounds like **dz** in *adze*.

☐ I practiced my flashcards today. (Add the new cards.)

LET'S PRACTICE

Write the first six Greek alphabet letters in order.

α β γ δ

ε ζ

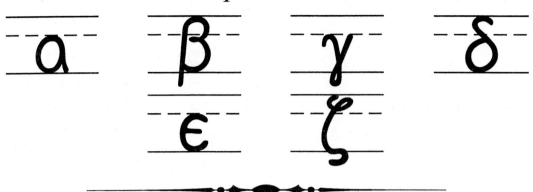

Draw lines through three Greek letters that are alike.

~~γ γ γ~~ δ α δ	γ δ δ ~~ζ ζ ζ~~	~~ε ε ε~~ β α α	~~β β β~~ δ γ δ
~~δ δ δ~~ γ β γ	ε β δ ~~α α α~~	~~ζ ζ ζ~~ β ε α	α ζ α ~~ε ε ε~~

Circle the names of the Greek letters.

ζ	zeta	alpha	epsilon	beta
δ	beta	gamma	epsilon	delta
ε	delta	epsilon	gamma	alpha

☐ I practiced my flashcards today.

MORE ALPHABET REVIEW

ETA

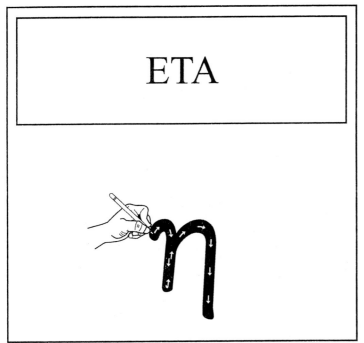

Write the letter *eta* across each line. As you write it, say "**ay**-ta."

It sounds like **a** in *late*.

THETA

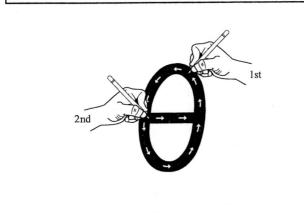

Write the letter *theta* across each line. As you write it, say "**thay**-ta."

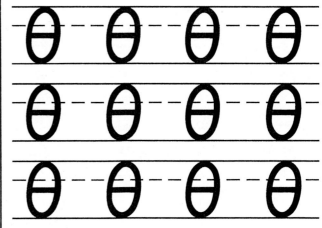

It sounds like **th** in *bath*.

☐ I practiced my flashcards today. (Add the new cards.)

LET'S PRACTICE

Write the first eight Greek alphabet letters in order.

Circle the correct letter names below the Greek letters.

η		θ		δ	
gamma	(eta)	(theta)	beta	alpha	(delta)
ζ		ε		β	
(zeta)	delta	eta	(epsilon)	(beta)	theta
γ		α		θ	
epsilon	(gamma)	(alpha)	gamma	zeta	(theta)

Look at the circled letter in each box. Which Greek letter comes next? Color it purple.

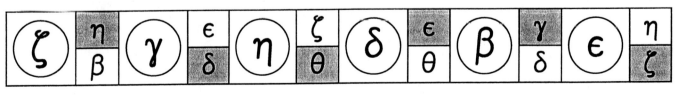

☐ I practiced my flashcards today.

MORE ALPHABET REVIEW

IOTA

Write the letter *iota* across each line. As you write it, say "ee-**o**-ta."

ι ι ι ι

ι ι ι ι

ι ι ι ι

It sounds like **i** in *pit*.

KAPPA

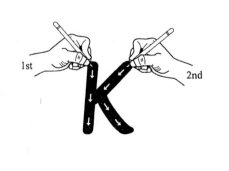

1st   2nd

Write the letter *kappa* across each line. As you write it, say "**kap**-pa."

K K K K

K K K K

K K K K

It sounds like **k** in *kite*.

☐ I practiced my flashcards today. (Add the new cards.)

LET'S PRACTICE

Write the first ten Greek alphabet letters in order.

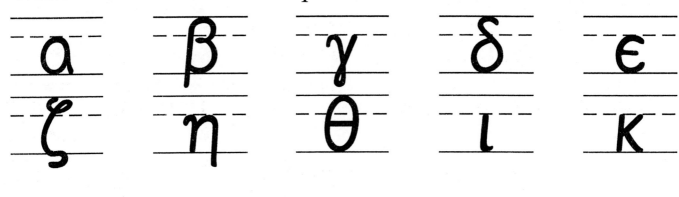

Write the names of the Greek letters.

α   alpha

β   beta

γ   gamma

δ   delta

ε   epsilon

ζ   zeta

η   eta

θ   theta

ι   iota

κ   kappa

☐   I practiced my flashcards today.

Greek Workbook - Level 2
Copyright © 1994 by Karen Mohs

MORE ALPHABET REVIEW

LAMBDA

1st
2nd

Write the letter *lambda* across each line. As you write it, say "**lamb**-da."

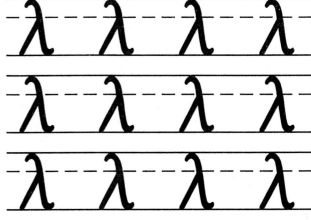

λ λ λ λ

λ λ λ λ

λ λ λ λ

It sounds like **l** in *lamb*.

MU

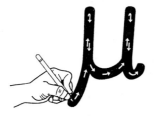

Write the letter *mu* across each line. As you write it, say "**moo**."

μ μ μ μ

μ μ μ μ

μ μ μ μ

It sounds like **m** in *man*.

☐ I practiced my flashcards today. (Add the new cards.)

LET'S PRACTICE

Write the first twelve Greek alphabet letters in order.

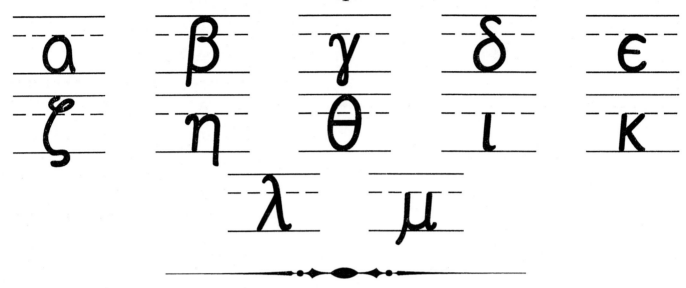

Circle the correct names of the Greek letters.

iota kappa ζ (zeta) epsilon	alpha lambda κ theta (kappa)	lambda (eta) η iota gamma
(mu) gamma μ kappa delta	beta (delta) δ theta mu	alpha zeta λ eta (lambda)
eta beta θ (theta) delta	(iota) epsilon ι gamma mu	alpha zeta ε beta (epsilon)

☐ I practiced my flashcards today.

Greek Workbook - Level 2
Copyright © 1994 by Karen Mohs

MORE ALPHABET REVIEW

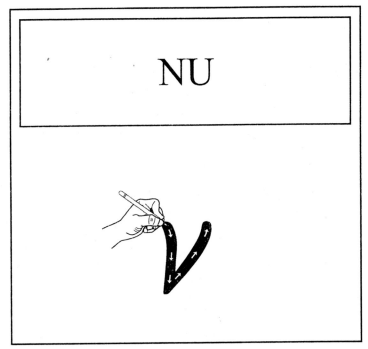

Write the letter *nu* across each line. As you write it, say **"noo."**

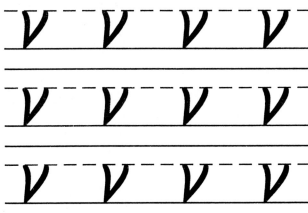

It sounds like **n** in *nice*.

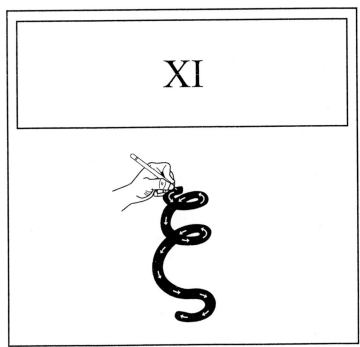

Write the letter *xi* across each line. As you write it, say **"ksee."**

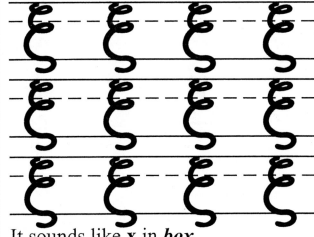

It sounds like **x** in *box*.

☐ I practiced my flashcards today. (Add the new cards.)

LET'S PRACTICE

Write the first fourteen Greek alphabet letters in order.

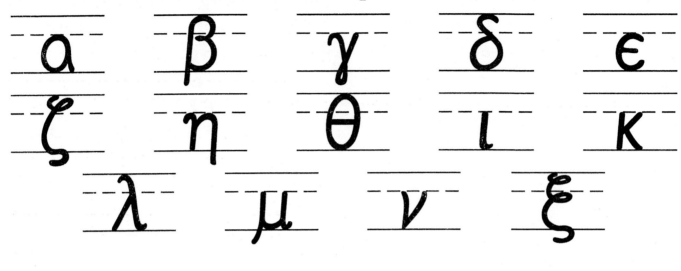

α β γ δ ε
ζ η θ ι κ
λ μ ν ξ

Draw lines from the Greek letters to their sounds.

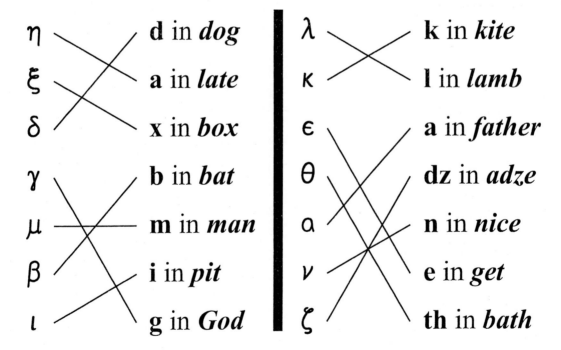

η	**d** in *dog*
ξ	**a** in *late*
δ	**x** in *box*
γ	**b** in *bat*
μ	**m** in *man*
β	**i** in *pit*
ι	**g** in *God*

λ	**k** in *kite*
κ	**l** in *lamb*
ε	**a** in *father*
θ	**dz** in *adze*
α	**n** in *nice*
ν	**e** in *get*
ζ	**th** in *bath*

☐ I practiced my flashcards today.

MORE ALPHABET REVIEW

OMICRON

Write the letter *omicron* across each line. As you write it, say "**ahm**-i-cron."

It sounds like **o** in *obey*.

PI

Write the letter *pi* across each line. As you write it, say "**pie**."

1st 2nd 3rd

It sounds like **p** in *pie*.

☐ I practiced my flashcards today. (Add the new cards.)

LET'S PRACTICE

Write the first sixteen Greek alphabet letters in order.

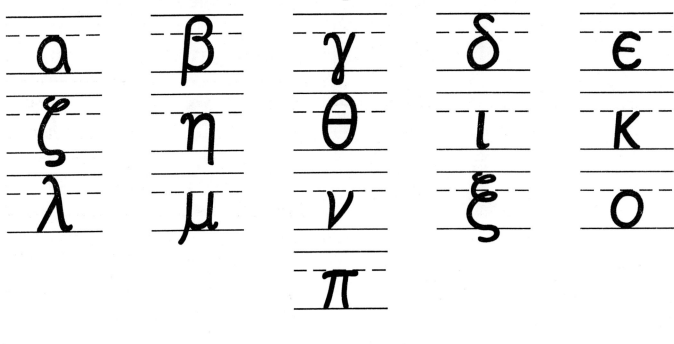

Circle the names of the Greek letters.

π	lambda	(pi)	eta	gamma
μ	nu	kappa	lambda	(mu)
o	(omicron)	alpha	theta	epsilon
ξ	beta	zeta	(xi)	delta
ν	iota	mu	alpha	(nu)

☐ I practiced my flashcards today.

16

MORE ALPHABET REVIEW

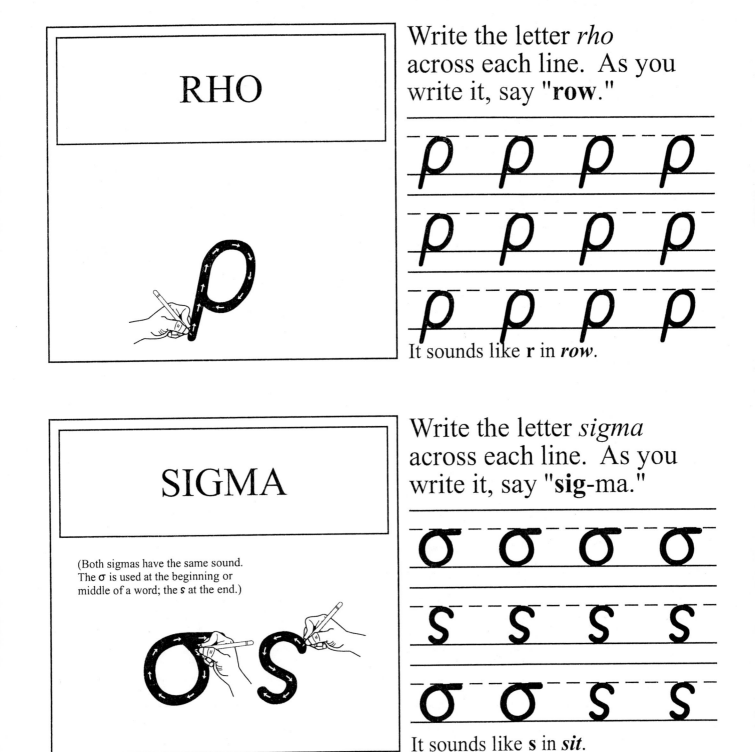

RHO

Write the letter *rho* across each line. As you write it, say **"row."**

ρ ρ ρ ρ

ρ ρ ρ ρ

ρ ρ ρ ρ

It sounds like **r** in *row*.

SIGMA

(Both sigmas have the same sound. The σ is used at the beginning or middle of a word; the **s** at the end.)

Write the letter *sigma* across each line. As you write it, say **"sig-ma."**

σ σ σ σ

s s s s

σ σ s s

It sounds like **s** in *sit*.

☐ I practiced my flashcards today. (Add the new cards.)

LET'S PRACTICE

Write the first eighteen Greek alphabet letters in order.

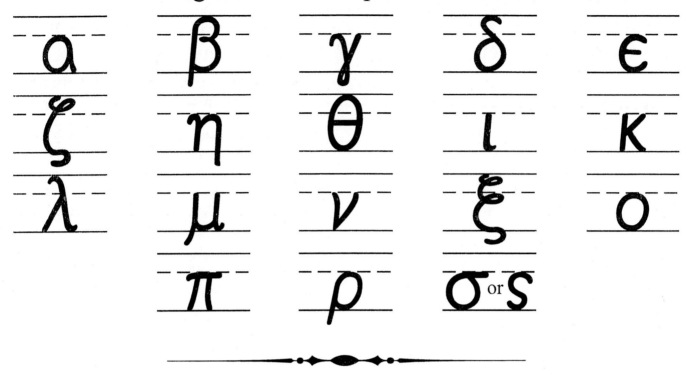

α   β   γ   δ   ε
ζ   η   θ   ι   κ
λ   μ   ν   ξ   ο
     π   ρ   σ or ς

Color the correct letters green.

xi	ζ	ξ	σ	ζ	ζ	δ	ξ	δ	ξ
rho	ρ	α	σ	ο	ρ	σ	ρ	α	σ
pi	γ	ζ	π	π	γ	ε	γ	π	ζ
sigma	σ	σ	ς	ρ	ο	σ	ι	ς	α
omicron	α	ο	σ	ο	σ	ρ	α	σ	ο
nu	ν	η	ν	π	ν	η	π	η	μ

☐ I practiced my flashcards today.

18

MORE ALPHABET REVIEW

TAU

Write the letter *tau* across each line. As you write it, say "**tou**."

T T T T

T T T T

T T T T

It sounds like **t** in *toy*.

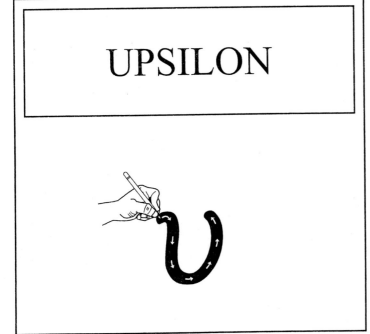

UPSILON

Write the letter *upsilon* across each line. As you write it, say "**up**-si-lon."

U U U U

U U U U

U U U U

It sounds like **oo** in *good*.

☐ I practiced my flashcards today. (Add the new cards.)

LET'S PRACTICE

Write the first twenty Greek alphabet letters in order.

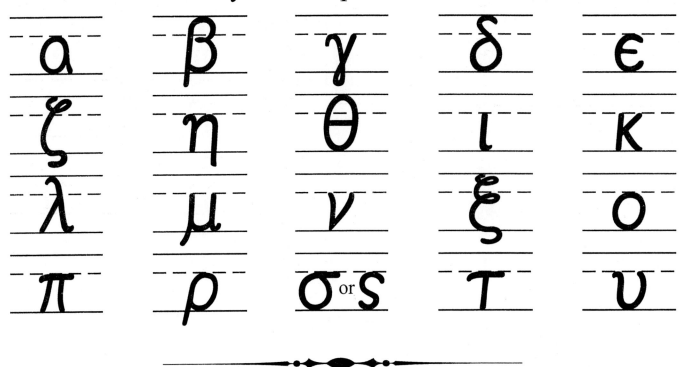

α   β   γ   δ   ε

ζ   η   θ   ι   κ

λ   μ   ν   ξ   ο

π   ρ   σ or ς   τ   υ

———————————◆●◆———————————

Circle the correct letter names below the Greek letters.

τ		ρ		υ	
eta	(tau)	(rho)	pi	(upsilon)	epsilon
ν		σ		ξ	
mu	(nu)	(sigma)	epsilon	zeta	(xi)
ο		μ		π	
(omicron)	alpha	nu	(mu)	(pi)	tau

☐ I practiced my flashcards today.

MORE ALPHABET REVIEW

PHI

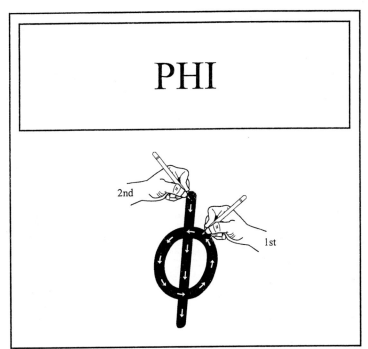

Write the letter *phi* across each line. As you write it, say **"fee."**

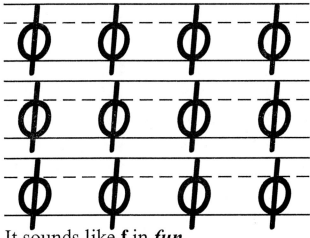

It sounds like **f** in *fun*.

CHI

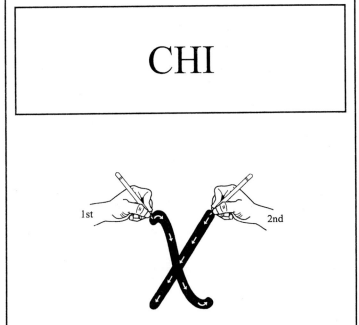

Write the letter *chi* across each line. As you write it, say **"kee."**

It sounds like the German **ch** in *Ach*.

☐ I practiced my flashcards today. (Add the new cards.)

LET'S PRACTICE

Write the first twenty-two Greek alphabet letters in order.

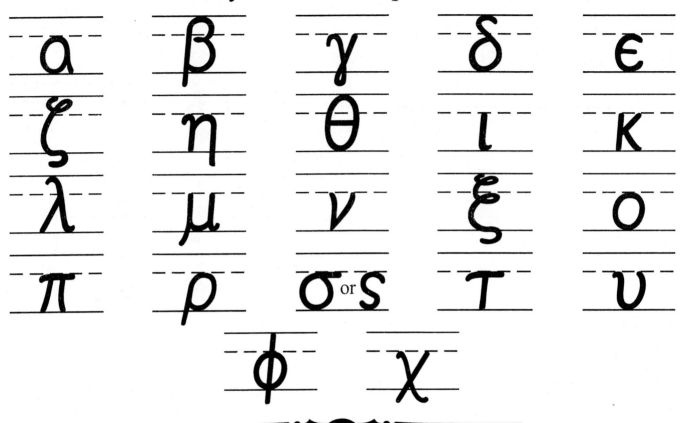

Draw lines from the Greek letters to their names.

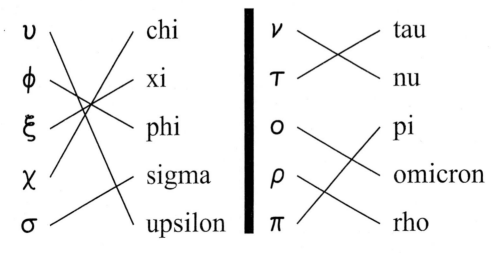

υ	chi
φ	xi
ξ	phi
χ	sigma
σ	upsilon

ν	tau
τ	nu
ο	pi
ρ	omicron
π	rho

☐ I practiced my flashcards today.

MORE ALPHABET REVIEW

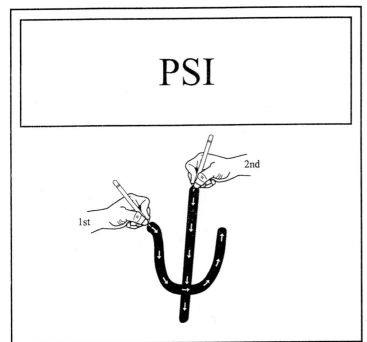

PSI

Write the letter *psi* across each line. As you write it, say **"psee."**

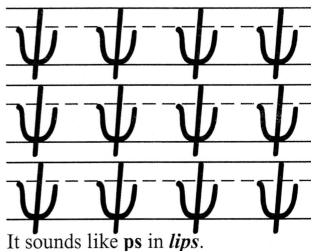

It sounds like **ps** in *lips*.

OMEGA

Write the letter *omega* across each line. As you write it, say "o-**may**-ga."

It sounds like **o** in *note*.

☐ I practiced my flashcards today. (Add the new cards.)

LET'S PRACTICE

Write all twenty-four Greek alphabet letters in order.

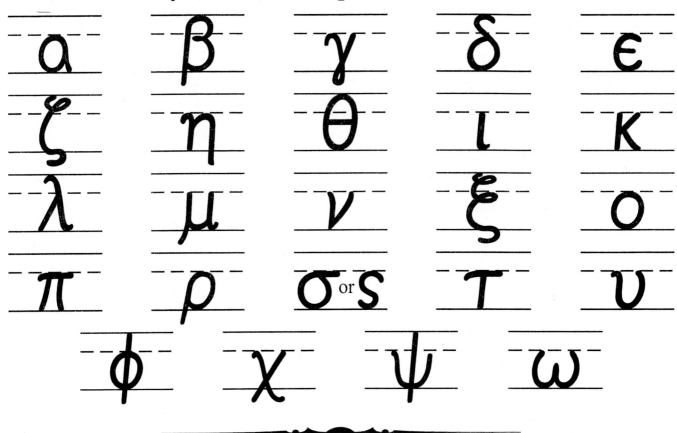

Look at the circled letter in each box. Which Greek letter comes next? Color it orange.

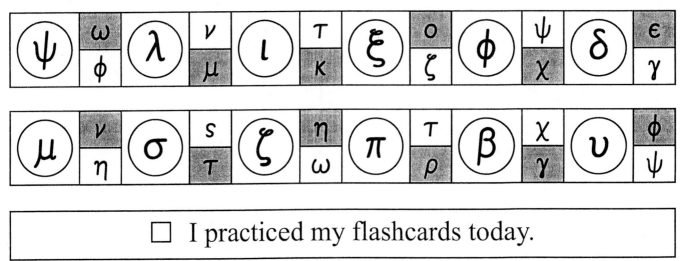

☐ I practiced my flashcards today.

LET'S PRACTICE

Circle all the Greek letters.

η   A   σ   β

λ

ξ   h

κ

ψ   f

τ   π

a   c

j   ζ   y

r

ι

υ

ω   φ

ε

d   g

μ

o   l

q

e

m   χ   γ

δ

i

θ   ρ   ν   z

☐ I practiced my flashcards today.

LET'S PRACTICE

Color the triangle blue if the letter name matches the letter at the top.

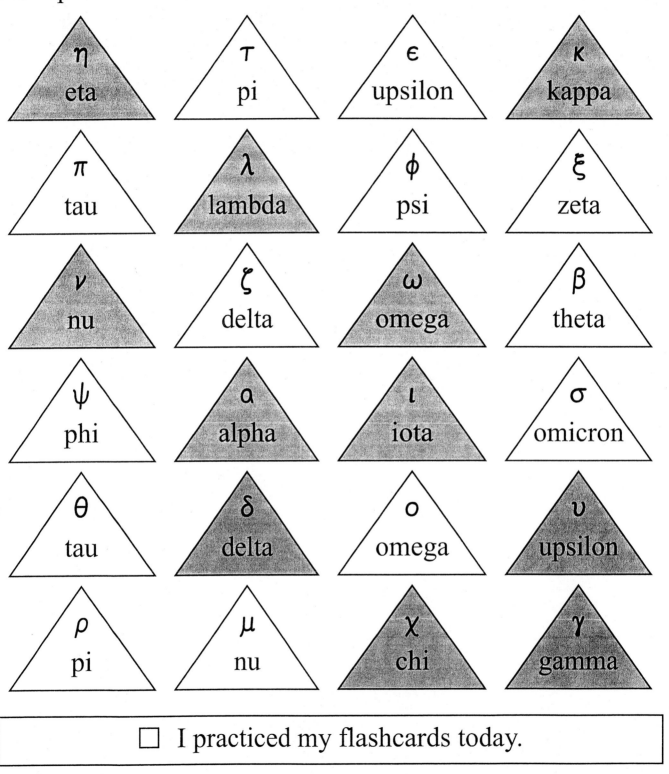

26

LET'S PRACTICE

Write the names of the Greek letters.

α   alpha _____

β   beta _____

γ   gamma _____

δ   delta _____

ε   epsilon _____

ζ   zeta _____

η   eta _____

θ   theta _____

ι   iota _____

κ   kappa _____

λ   lambda _____

μ   mu _____

ν   nu _____

ξ   xi _____

ο   omicron _____

π   pi _____

ρ   rho _____

σ   sigma _____

τ   tau _____

υ   upsilon _____

φ   phi _____

χ   chi _____

ψ   psi _____

ω   omega _____

☐ I practiced my flashcards today.

LET'S PRACTICE

Write the Greek letters on the lines beside their names.

iota	ι	eta	η
pi	π	omicron	ο
nu	ν	tau	τ
omega	ω	mu	μ
epsilon	ε	kappa	κ
phi	φ	chi	χ
sigma	σ or ς	xi	ξ
theta	θ	upsilon	υ
psi	ψ	zeta	ζ
lambda	λ	rho	ρ

☐ I practiced my flashcards today.

LET'S PRACTICE

Circle the correct names of the Greek letters.

(lambda) tau λ iota sigma	rho omega σ alpha (sigma)	nu epsilon ι (iota) lambda
pi psi ρ (rho) omicron	(psi) upsilon ψ epsilon nu	chi (xi) ξ pi phi
theta omicron ω tau (omega)	nu (omicron) o omega sigma	pi lambda τ (tau) delta
(theta) tau θ delta xi	phi omega υ (upsilon) nu	beta (eta) η zeta gamma
(chi) eta χ kappa tau	omicron nu μ (mu) delta	chi (phi) φ psi gamma
mu epsilon ν chi (nu)	epsilon (kappa) κ chi upsilon	iota tau π (pi) phi

☐ I practiced my flashcards today.

LET'S PRACTICE

Draw lines from the Greek letters to their sounds.

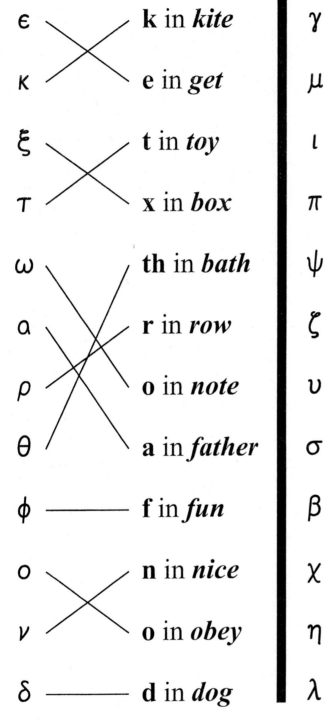

ε   k in *kite*

κ   e in *get*

ξ   t in *toy*

τ   x in *box*

ω   th in *bath*

α   r in *row*

ρ   o in *note*

θ   a in *father*

φ   f in *fun*

ο   n in *nice*

ν   o in *obey*

δ   d in *dog*

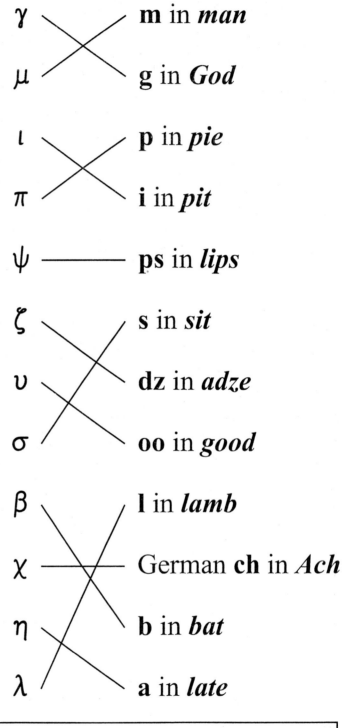

γ   m in *man*

μ   g in *God*

ι   p in *pie*

π   i in *pit*

ψ   ps in *lips*

ζ   s in *sit*

υ   dz in *adze*

σ   oo in *good*

β   l in *lamb*

χ   German ch in *Ach*

η   b in *bat*

λ   a in *late*

☐ I practiced my flashcards today.

30

LET'S PRACTICE

Circle the names of the Greek letters.

μ	iota	nu	(mu)	lambda
π	(pi)	kappa	tau	rho
ψ	eta	zeta	xi	(psi)
ρ	alpha	kappa	gamma	(rho)
ν	upsilon	(nu)	phi	beta
ξ	(xi)	epsilon	sigma	eta
υ	mu	(upsilon)	psi	epsilon
κ	psi	beta	(kappa)	chi
τ	lambda	pi	omega	(tau)
o	(omicron)	delta	sigma	rho
ω	omicron	(omega)	mu	nu
φ	theta	pi	tau	(phi)
λ	iota	gamma	(lambda)	theta
χ	(chi)	xi	phi	zeta
σ	delta	alpha	omicron	(sigma)

☐ I practiced my flashcards today.

LET'S PRACTICE

Circle the correct letter names below the Greek letters.

λ		o		ν	
tau	(lambda)	(omicron)	omega	upsilon	(nu)
υ		α		ψ	
(upsilon)	nu	iota	(alpha)	(psi)	upsilon
μ		τ		θ	
(mu)	nu	pi	(tau)	phi	(theta)
ρ		ι		ω	
(rho)	pi	(iota)	lambda	(omega)	omicron
η		χ		γ	
nu	(eta)	kappa	(chi)	(gamma)	omega
ε		ξ		φ	
(epsilon)	eta	zeta	(xi)	theta	(phi)
δ		κ		π	
(delta)	psi	chi	(kappa)	(pi)	tau

☐ I practiced my flashcards today.

LET'S PRACTICE

Color the correct letters pink.

theta	θ	τ	θ	η	τ	η	η	θ	τ
pi	τ	π	φ	π	τ	π	π	φ	τ
kappa	χ	χ	κ	ψ	χ	κ	χ	ψ	ψ
psi	φ	ψ	φ	π	φ	π	ψ	π	ψ
phi	π	φ	π	φ	ξ	φ	φ	π	ξ
beta	β	α	β	α	θ	β	θ	α	θ
mu	ν	ν	ω	ν	μ	ω	μ	ν	ω
chi	ξ	χ	κ	χ	ξ	κ	χ	ξ	χ
delta	β	ζ	β	δ	β	δ	β	δ	ζ
zeta	ζ	ξ	ζ	ξ	ζ	γ	ξ	γ	γ
upsilon	υ	ν	υ	υ	ω	ν	ω	ν	υ
omega	ω	ο	ω	σ	ω	ο	ω	σ	ο
eta	ε	η	ε	η	ε	α	η	η	α
sigma	ο	ς	ο	ς	ψ	ο	σ	σ	ψ
xi	ξ	χ	ξ	χ	ξ	ξ	κ	χ	κ

☐ I practiced my flashcards today.

LET'S PRACTICE

Draw lines from the Greek letters to their names.

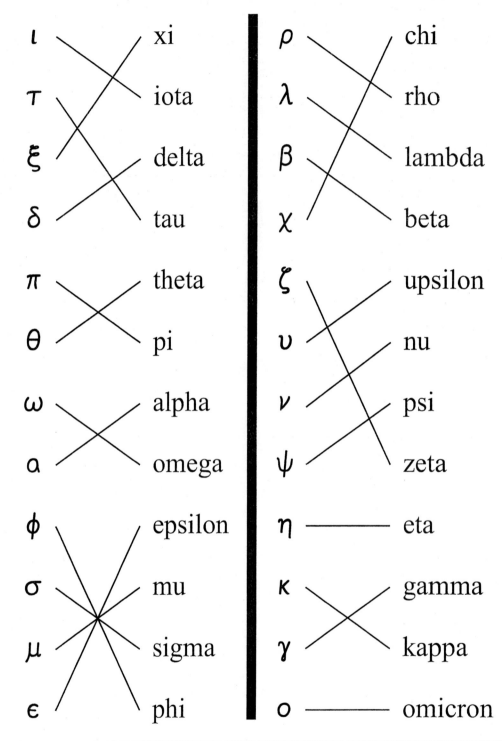

ι	xi	ρ	chi
τ	iota	λ	rho
ξ	delta	β	lambda
δ	tau	χ	beta
π	theta	ζ	upsilon
θ	pi	υ	nu
ω	alpha	ν	psi
α	omega	ψ	zeta
φ	epsilon	η — eta	
σ	mu	κ	gamma
μ	sigma	γ	kappa
ε	phi	ο — omicron	

☐ I practiced my flashcards today.

Greek Workbook - Level 2
Copyright © 1994 by Karen Mohs

LET'S PRACTICE

Write all twenty-four Greek alphabet letters in order.

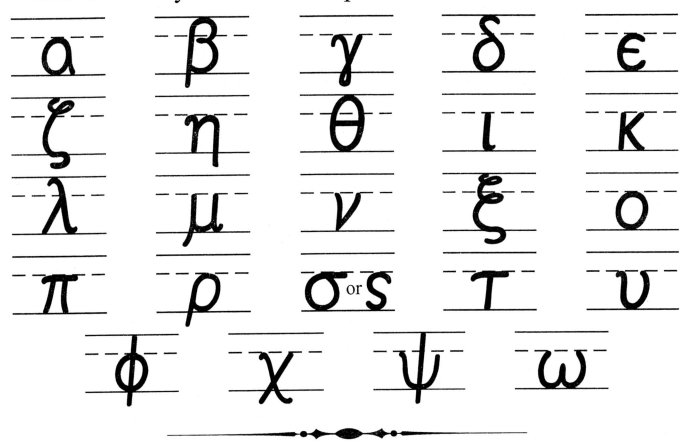

Look at the circled letter in each box. Which Greek letter comes next? Color it yellow.

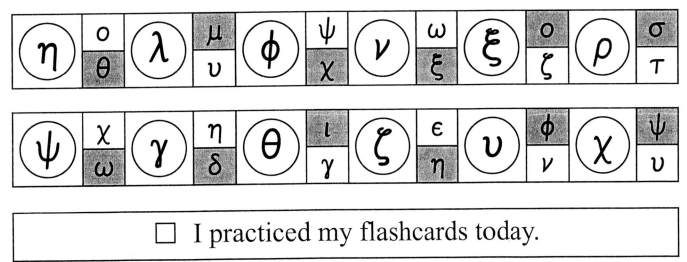

☐ I practiced my flashcards today.

LET'S PRACTICE

Blacken the boxes with Greek letters to find a message.

σ	φ	S	β	e	γ	e	ζ	ξ	γ	!	δ	π	ζ	θ	ψ	λ
ζ	I	ψ	ξ	δ	ζ	μ	φ	c	μ	π	a	γ	n	ψ	μ	δ
l	e	φ	a	r	n	ψ	β	G	ζ	r	e	θ	e	μ	k	!

Connect the dots.

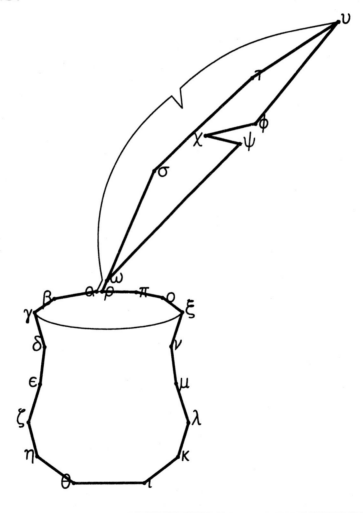

☐ I practiced my flashcards today.

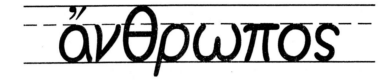

means

a man

It sounds like **an**-thro-pos.

Remember: The ο and the ω both have a long o sound, but the ω is held longer.

Circle the Greek words that mean **a man**.

ἀθέμιτος   ἀγαπητός   (ἄνθρωπος)
(ἄνθρωπος)   ἀγιασμός   ἀθέμιτος
ἀγαπητός   ἀθέμιτος   ἀγιασμός
ἀγιασμός   (ἄνθρωπος)   ἀγαπητός

☐   I practiced my flashcards today. (Add the new card.)

More Practice
with
ἄνθρωπος

Write the Greek word that means **a man**.*

ἄνθρωπος   ἄνθρωπος

ἄνθρωπος   ἄνθρωπος

ἄνθρωπος   ἄνθρωπος

ἄνθρωπος   ἄνθρωπος

ἄνθρωπος   ἄνθρωπος

ἄνθρωπος   ἄνθρωπος

*The student should first write the letters of the Greek word. Then, much the same as crossing a *t* or dotting an *i* in English, the accents and breathing marks (the little symbols above the letters) are to be added before continuing to the next word.

☐ I practiced my flashcards today.

Greek Workbook - Level 2
Copyright © 1994 by Karen Mohs

LET'S PRACTICE

Circle **yes** or **no**.

yes [no]   1. ἄνθρωπος means **a house**.

yes [no]   2. ἄνθρωπος means **a barn**.

yes [no]   3. ἄνθρωπος means **a dog**.

[yes] no   4. ἄνθρωπος means **a man**.

———————◆·◆·●·◆·◆———————

Fill in the missing letters on the Greek word that means **a man**.

ἄνθρωπος

———————◆·◆·●·◆·◆———————

Draw a line from the Greek word to its meaning.

a girl

ἄνθρωπος ———————— a man

an elephant

☐ I practiced my flashcards today.

LET'S PRACTICE

Circle the Greek word to match the meaning.

a man
ἀγαπητός
ἁγιασμός
(ἄνθρωπος)
ἀθέμιτος

Check the blank if the sentence is true.

_____   1. ἄνθρωπος means **a cow**.

✔_____   2. ἄνθρωπος means **a man**.

_____   3. ἄνθρωπος means **a mule**.

Write the Greek word to match the sound.

an-thro-pos

☐ I practiced my flashcards today.

LET'S PRACTICE

Circle the meaning of the Greek word.

ἄνθρωπος	
a car	(a man)

Write the Greek word.

a man

Circle the Greek words to match the meaning.

	ἄνθρωπος	ἀγαπητός
a man	ἀγαπητός	ἁγιασμός
	ἀθέμιτος	ἄνθρωπος

☐ I practiced my flashcards today.

LET'S PRACTICE

Write the meaning of the Greek word.

ἄνθρωπος   <u>a man   </u>

Color the boxes green that have the same Greek word as the word in the big box.

| ἄνθρωπος | ἄνθρωπος | ἀγαπητός |
| | ἀθέμιτος | ἄνθρωπος |

Connect the Greek words to their meaning in the oval.

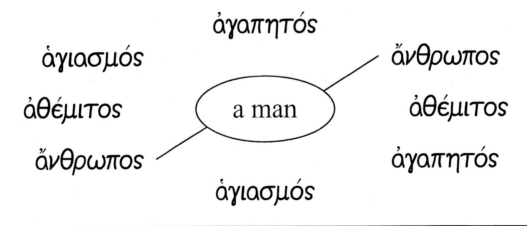

ἀγαπητός

ἀγιασμός   ἄνθρωπος

ἀθέμιτος   (a man)   ἀθέμιτος

ἄνθρωπος   ἀγαπητός

ἀγιασμός

☐ I practiced my flashcards today.

Greek Workbook - Level 2
Copyright © 1994 by Karen Mohs

means

a brother

It sounds like a-del-**fos**.

Circle the Greek words that mean **a brother**.

ἄδικος   ἄνθρωπος   ἄδικος

ἄδολος   (ἀδελφός)   ἄδολος

ἄνθρωπος   ἄδικος   (ἀδελφός)

(ἀδελφός)   ἄδολος   ἄνθρωπος

☐ I practiced my flashcards today. (Add the new card.)

More Practice
with
ἀδελφός

Write the Greek word that means **a brother**.

ἀδελφός   ἀδελφός

ἀδελφός   ἀδελφός

ἀδελφός   ἀδελφός

ἀδελφός   ἀδελφός

ἀδελφός   ἀδελφός

ἀδελφός   ἀδελφός

ἀδελφός   ἀδελφός

☐ I practiced my flashcards today.

LET'S PRACTICE

Connect the Greek words to their meanings in the ovals.

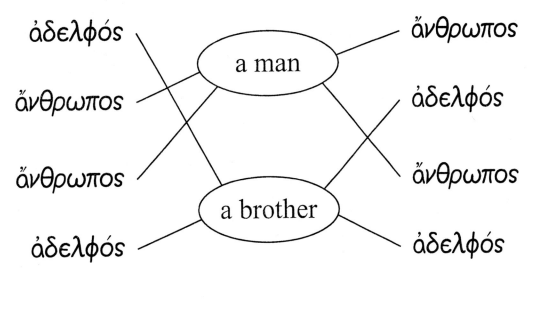

Color the boxes pink that have the same Greek words as the words in the big boxes.

ἀδελφός	ἄδικος	ἀδελφός
	ἀδελφός	ἄδολος

ἄνθρωπος	ἄνθρωπος	ἀγαπητός
	ἀθέμιτος	ἄνθρωπος

☐ I practiced my flashcards today.

LET'S PRACTICE

Write the meanings of the Greek words.

ἄνθρωπος   <u>a man</u>

ἀδελφός   <u>a brother</u>

———————◆●◆———————

Write the Greek words to match the sounds.

a-del-**fos**   ἀδελφός

an-thro-pos   ἄνθρωπος

☐ I practiced my flashcards today.

Greek Workbook - Level 2
Copyright © 1994 by Karen Mohs

LET'S PRACTICE

Circle **yes** or **no**.

yes [no] 1. ἀδελφός means **a roof**.

yes [no] 2. ἄνθρωπος means **a pan**.

[yes] no 3. ἀδελφός means **a brother**.

yes [no] 4. ἄνθρωπος means **a mouse**.

yes [no] 5. ἀδελφός means **a father**.

[yes] no 6. ἄνθρωπος means **a man**.

yes [no] 7. ἀδελφός means **a sister**.

Fill in the missing letters. Then write what the words mean.

ἄνθρωπος

It means _a man_

ἀδελφός

It means _a brother_

☐ I practiced my flashcards today.

LET'S PRACTICE

Draw lines from the Greek words to their meanings.

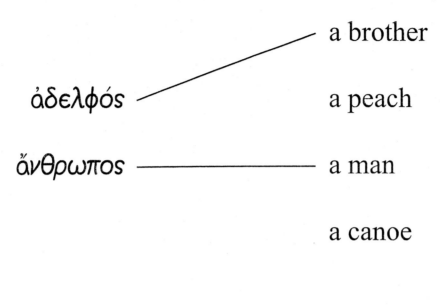

ἀδελφός   a brother

                 a peach

ἄνθρωπος —————— a man

                 a canoe

Circle the Greek words to match the meanings.

a brother	a man
ἄδικος	ἀδελφός
(ἀδελφός)	(ἄνθρωπος)
ἄδολος	ἀθέμιτος
ἄνθρωπος	ἁγιασμός

☐ I practiced my flashcards today.

LET'S PRACTICE

Draw lines from the sounds to their Greek words.

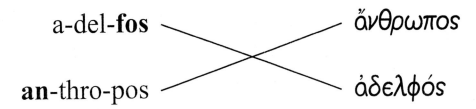

a-del-**fos**   ἄνθρωπος

an-thro-pos   ἀδελφός

Check the blank if the sentence is true.

_____ 1. ἄνθρωπος means **a cart**.

_____ 2. ἀδελφός means **a wreath**.

___✓___ 3. ἄνθρωπος means **a man**.

_____ 4. ἀδελφός means **a roadway**.

_____ 5. ἄνθρωπος means **a party**.

___✓___ 6. ἀδελφός means **a brother**.

☐ I practiced my flashcards today.

LET'S PRACTICE

Write the Greek words.

a man

a brother

Circle the meanings of the Greek words.

ἀδελφός	
a box	(a brother)

ἄνθρωπος	
(a man)	a pen

☐ I practiced my flashcards today.

50

LET'S PRACTICE

Circle the Greek words to match the meanings.

a brother	ἄδολος	(ἀδελφός)
	(ἀδελφός)	ἄνθρωπος
	ἄδικος	ἄδολος

a man	(ἄνθρωπος)	ἀγαπητός
	ἁγιασμός	ἀθέμιτος
	ἀδελφός	(ἄνθρωπος)

———— ◆ ————

Fill in the blanks with the Greek words from the box.

ἄνθρωπος	ἀδελφός

1. __ἀδελφός__ means **a brother**.

2. __ἄνθρωπος__ means **a man**.

☐ I practiced my flashcards today.

LET'S PRACTICE

Color the tickets green if the words inside mean the same.

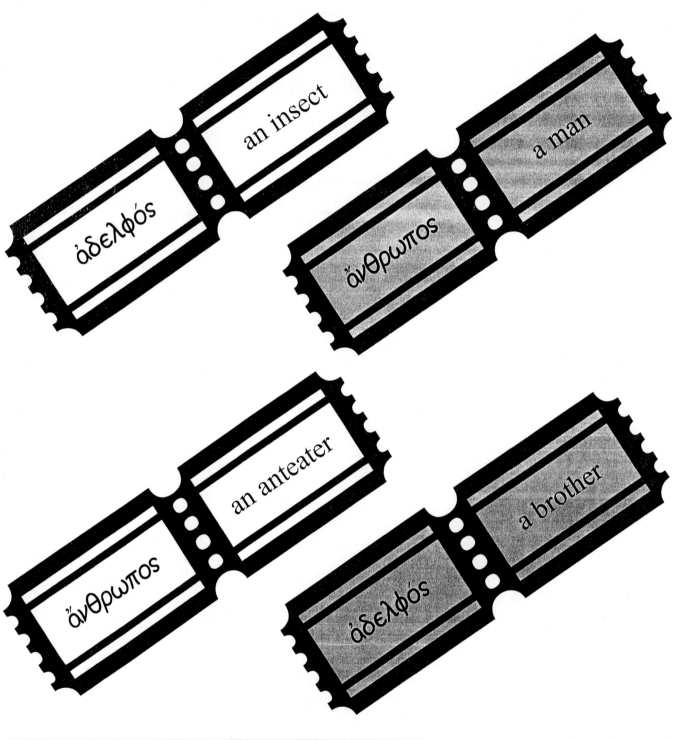

| | I practiced my flashcards today. |

ἀπόστολος

means

an apostle

It sounds like a-**po**-sto-los.

Circle the Greek words that mean **an apostle**.

(ἀπόστολος)　ἄπιστος　(ἀπόστολος)
ἄπιστος　ἄνθρωπος　ἀποστάσιον
ἀποστάσιον　ἀπόδεκτος　ἀδελφός
ἀδελφός　(ἀπόστολος)　ἄνθρωπος

☐ I practiced my flashcards today. (Add the new card.)

More Practice
with
ἀπόστολος

Write the Greek word that means **an apostle**.

ἀπόστολος   ἀπόστολος

ἀπόστολος   ἀπόστολος

ἀπόστολος   ἀπόστολος

ἀπόστολος   ἀπόστολος

ἀπόστολος   ἀπόστολος

ἀπόστολος   ἀπόστολος

ἀπόστολος   ἀπόστολος

☐ I practiced my flashcards today.

LET'S PRACTICE

Circle the Greek words to match the meanings.

an apostle	(ἀπόστολος)	ἀδελφός
	ἀδελφός	(ἀπόστολος)

a man	ἀδελφός	(ἄνθρωπος)
	(ἄνθρωπος)	ἀδελφός

a brother	(ἀδελφός)	ἄνθρωπος
	(ἀδελφός)	ἄνθρωπος

Circle **yes** or **no**.

yes [no] 1. ἀπόστολος means **a missle**.

yes [no] 2. ἄνθρωπος means **a race**.

[yes] no 3. ἀδελφός means **a brother**.

yes [no] 4. ἀπόστολος means **a mother**.

[yes] no 5. ἀπόστολος means **an apostle**.

[yes] no 6. ἄνθρωπος means **a man**.

yes [no] 7. ἀδελφός means **a dish**.

☐ I practiced my flashcards today.

LET'S PRACTICE

Write the Greek words to match the sounds.

an-thro-pos

a-**po**-sto-los

a-del-**fos**

Write the meanings of the Greek words.

ἄνθρωπος   a man

ἀδελφός   a brother

ἀπόστολος   an apostle

☐ I practiced my flashcards today.

LET'S PRACTICE

Connect the Greek words to their meanings in the ovals.

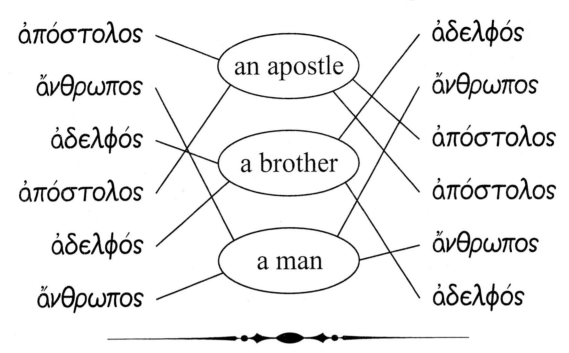

Fill in the missing letters. Then write what the words mean.

ἄν<u>θ</u>ρω<u>π</u>ος

It means <u>a man</u>

ἀ<u>π</u>όσ<u>το</u>λος

It means <u>an apostle</u>

ἀ<u>δ</u>ε<u>λ</u>φ<u>ό</u>ς

It means <u>a brother</u>

☐ I practiced my flashcards today.

LET'S PRACTICE

Draw lines from the Greek words to their meanings.

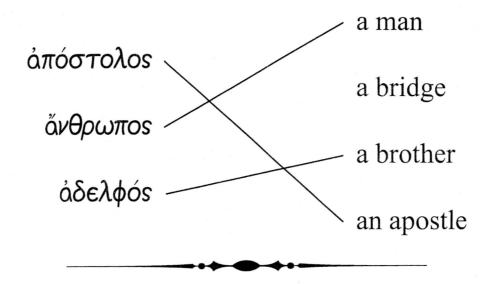

ἀπόστολος   a man

                a bridge

ἄνθρωπος

                a brother

ἀδελφός   an apostle

Color the boxes purple that have the same Greek words as the words in the big boxes.

ἄνθρωπος	ἀθέμιτος	**ἄνθρωπος**
	ἀγαπητός	**ἄνθρωπος**

ἀπόστολος	**ἀπόστολος**	**ἀπόστολος**
	ἀποστάσιον	ἀπόδεκτος

ἀδελφός	**ἀδελφός**	ἄδολος
	ἄδικος	**ἀδελφός**

☐ I practiced my flashcards today.

Greek Workbook - Level 2
Copyright © 1994 by Karen Mohs

LET'S PRACTICE

Circle the Greek words to match the meanings.

a man
ἀπόστολος
ἀδελφός
ἀγιασμός
(ἄνθρωπος)

an apostle
ἀποστάσιον
(ἀπόστολος)
ἀδελφός
ἄνθρωπος

a brother
(ἀδελφός)
ἄνθρωπος
ἄδολος
ἀπόστολος

Draw lines from the sounds to their Greek words.

a-del-**fos** ——————— ἀδελφός

a-**po**-sto-los ——————— ἀπόστολος

an-thro-pos ——————— ἄνθρωπος

☐ I practiced my flashcards today.

LET'S PRACTICE

Check the blank if the sentence is true.

    _____ 1. ἀπόστολος means **a pie**.

    ✓_____ 2. ἀδελφός means **a brother**.

    ✓_____ 3. ἀπόστολος means **an apostle**.

    _____ 4. ἄνθρωπος means **a bone**.

    _____ 5. ἀπόστολος means **a winner**.

    ✓_____ 6. ἄνθρωπος means **a man**.

    _____ 7. ἀδελφός means **a lake**.

Write the Greek words.

an apostle   ἀπόστολος

a brother   ἀδελφός

a man   ἄνθρωπος

☐ I practiced my flashcards today.

LET'S PRACTICE

Circle the meanings of the Greek words.

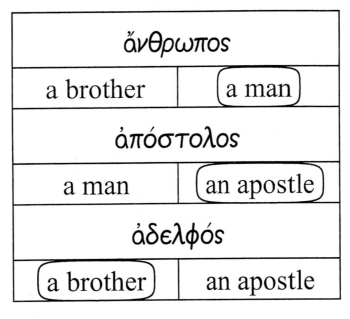

ἄνθρωπος	
a brother	(a man)
ἀπόστολος	
a man	(an apostle)
ἀδελφός	
(a brother)	an apostle

❖

Fill in the blanks with the Greek words from the box.

ἄνθρωπος	ἀπόστολος	ἀδελφός

1. **ἀπόστολος** means **an apostle**.

2. **ἄνθρωπος** means **a man**.

3. **ἀδελφός** means **a brother**.

☐ I practiced my flashcards today.

LET'S PRACTICE

Write the Greek words on the pails.

a brother

ἀδελφός

a man

ἄνθρωπος

an apostle

ἀπόστολος

☐ I practiced my flashcards today.

means

I see

It sounds like **ble**-po.

Circle the Greek words that mean **I see**.

βέλος   (βλέπω)   βάπτω
βάπτω   βέλος   βάλλω
(βλέπω)   βάλλω   βέλος
βάλλω   βάπτω   (βλέπω)

☐   I practiced my flashcards today. (Add the new card.)

More Practice
with
βλέπω

Write the Greek word that means **I see**.

βλέπω   βλέπω

βλέπω   βλέπω

βλέπω   βλέπω

βλέπω   βλέπω

βλέπω   βλέπω

βλέπω   βλέπω

βλέπω   βλέπω

☐ I practiced my flashcards today.

64

LET'S PRACTICE

Check the blank if the sentence is true.

✓   1. βλέπω means **I see**.

✓   2. ἀπόστολος means **an apostle**.

_____ 3. ἀδελφός means **a foot**.

_____ 4. βλέπω means **I rest**.

✓   5. ἀδελφός means **a brother**.

✓   6. ἄνθρωπος means **a man**.

_____ 7. ἀπόστολος means **a mansion**.

———————◆———————

Write the Greek words to match the sounds.

ble-po   βλέπω

a-del-**fos**   ἀδελφός

an-thro-pos   ἄνθρωπος

a-**po**-sto-los   ἀπόστολος

☐ I practiced my flashcards today.

LET'S PRACTICE

Circle the Greek words to match the meanings.

a brother	βλέπω	⟨ἀδελφός⟩
	ἀπόστολος	ἄνθρωπος

an apostle	⟨ἀπόστολος⟩	βλέπω
	ἄνθρωπος	ἀδελφός

I see	ἄνθρωπος	ἀπόστολος
	ἀδελφός	⟨βλέπω⟩

———————◆◆◆———————

Connect the Greek words to their meanings in the ovals.

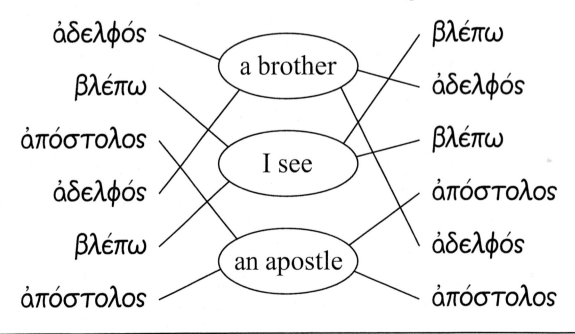

□ I practiced my flashcards today.

LET'S PRACTICE

Write the meanings of the Greek words.

ἀπόστολος <u>an apostle</u>

ἄνθρωπος <u>a man</u>

βλέπω <u>I see</u>

ἀδελφός <u>a brother</u>

―――――――――◆―――――――――

Draw lines from the Greek words to their meanings.

βλέπω   a brother

ἀδελφός   I see

ἄνθρωπος   an apostle

ἀπόστολος   a man

☐ I practiced my flashcards today.

LET'S PRACTICE

Fill in the missing letters. Then write what the words mean.

ἀδελφός

It means a brother

βλέπω

It means I see

ἀπόστολος

It means an apostle

———— ◆ ● ◆ ————

Circle the meanings of the Greek words.

ἀπόστολος		ἄνθρωπος	
(an apostle)	a man	I see	(a man)

βλέπω		ἀδελφός	
(I see)	a brother	(a brother)	an apostle

☐ I practiced my flashcards today.

LET'S PRACTICE

Write the Greek words.

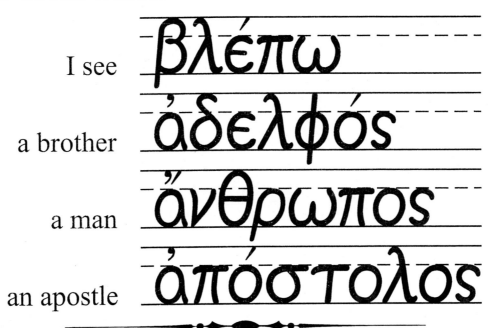

I see _____ βλέπω

a brother _____ ἀδελφός

a man _____ ἄνθρωπος

an apostle _____ ἀπόστολος

Circle the Greek words to match the meanings.

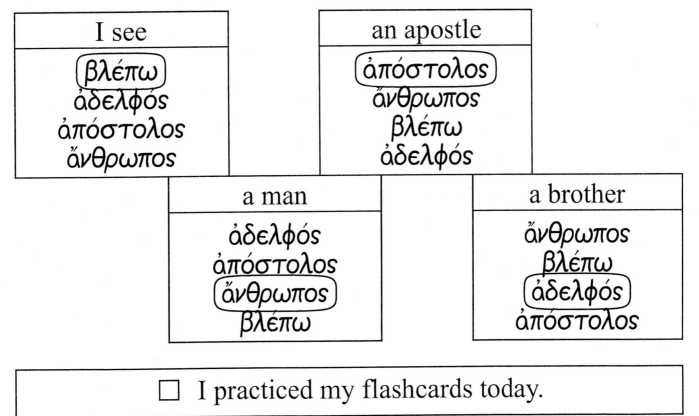

I see	an apostle
βλέπω	ἀπόστολος
ἀδελφός	ἄνθρωπος
ἀπόστολος	βλέπω
ἄνθρωπος	ἀδελφός

a man	a brother
ἀδελφός	ἄνθρωπος
ἀπόστολος	βλέπω
ἄνθρωπος	ἀδελφός
βλέπω	ἀπόστολος

☐ I practiced my flashcards today.

LET'S PRACTICE

Color the boxes blue that have the same Greek words as the words in the big boxes.

βλέπω	βάπτω	βέλος
	βλέπω	βλέπω

ἀδελφός	ἄδικος	ἄδολος
	ἀδελφός	ἀδελφός

ἀπόστολος	ἀπόδεκτος	ἀπόστολος
	ἀπόστολος	ἀποστάσιον

Draw lines from the sounds to their Greek words.

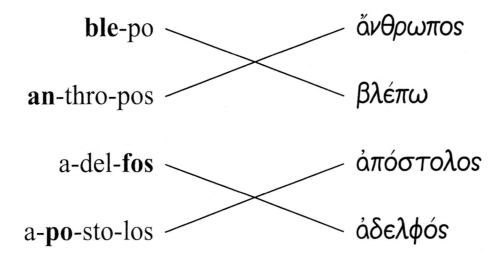

ble-po   ἄνθρωπος

an-thro-pos   βλέπω

a-del-**fos**   ἀπόστολος

a-**po**-sto-los   ἀδελφός

☐ I practiced my flashcards today.

LET'S PRACTICE

Fill in the blanks with the Greek words from the box.

ἀδελφός	βλέπω	ἀπόστολος

1. __βλέπω__ means **I see**.

2. __ἀπόστολος__ means **an apostle**.

3. __ἀδελφός__ means **a brother**.

Circle **yes** or **no**.

yes **no** 1. ἀπόστολος means **a monkey**.

yes no 2. ἄνθρωπος means **a man**.

yes no 3. ἀδελφός means **a brother**.

yes no 4. βλέπω means **I see**.

yes **no** 5. ἀδελφός means **a cloud**.

yes **no** 6. βλέπω means **I sit**.

yes no 7. ἀπόστολος means **an apostle**.

☐ I practiced my flashcards today.

LET'S PRACTICE

Color the bells pink if the words inside mean the same.

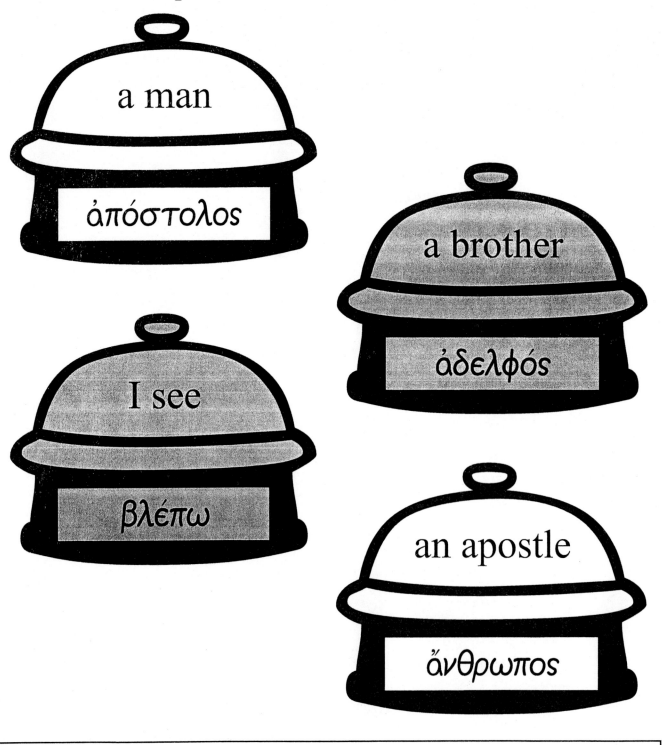

a man

ἀπόστολος

a brother

ἀδελφός

I see

βλέπω

an apostle

ἄνθρωπος

☐ I practiced my flashcards today.

means

I know

It sounds like ghi-**no**-sko.

Circle the Greek words that mean **I know**.

γίνομαι	γογγύζω	γαμέω
γαμέω	(γινώσκω)	γογγύζω
γογγύζω	γίνομαι	(γινώσκω)
(γινώσκω)	γαμέω	γίνομαι

☐ I practiced my flashcards today. (Add the new card.)

More Practice
with
γινώσκω

Write the Greek word that means **I know**.

γινώσκω γινώσκω

γινώσκω γινώσκω

γινώσκω γινώσκω

γινώσκω γινώσκω

γινώσκω γινώσκω

γινώσκω γινώσκω

γινώσκω γινώσκω

☐ I practiced my flashcards today.

Greek Workbook - Level 2
Copyright © 1994 by Karen Mohs

LET'S PRACTICE

Connect the Greek words to their meanings in the ovals.

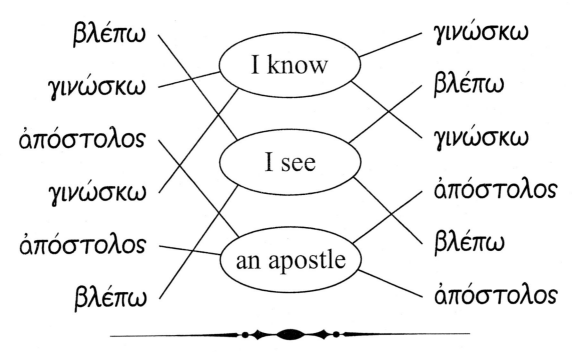

βλέπω   γινώσκω

γινώσκω   I know   βλέπω

ἀπόστολος   γινώσκω

γινώσκω   I see   ἀπόστολος

ἀπόστολος   βλέπω

βλέπω   an apostle   ἀπόστολος

Circle the Greek words to match the meanings.

a man	ἀπόστολος	βλέπω
	(ἄνθρωπος)	γινώσκω

I know	ἄνθρωπος	(γινώσκω)
	ἀδελφός	βλέπω

I see	γινώσκω	ἄνθρωπος
	(βλέπω)	ἀπόστολος

☐ I practiced my flashcards today.

LET'S PRACTICE

Write the meanings of the Greek words.

βλέπω   <u>I see</u>

γινώσκω   <u>I know</u>

ἀδελφός   <u>a brother</u>

ἀπόστολος <u>an apostle</u>

ἄνθρωπος <u>a man</u>

———————— ◆ ————————

Write the Greek words to match the sounds.

a-**po**-sto-los   <u>ἀπόστολος</u>

ghi-**no**-sko   <u>γινώσκω</u>

ble-po   <u>βλέπω</u>

a-del-**fos**   <u>ἀδελφός</u>

☐ I practiced my flashcards today.

LET'S PRACTICE

Fill in the missing letters. Then write what the words mean.

βλέπω

It means I see

ἀπόστολος

It means an apostle

γινώσκω

It means I know

———— ◆ ————

Check the blank if the sentence is true.

_✔___ 1. ἀπόστολος means **an apostle**.

_✔___ 2. γινώσκω means **I know**.

_✔___ 3. βλέπω means **I see**.

_____ 4. ἄνθρωπος means **a rabbit**.

_____ 5. γινώσκω means **I ski**.

_✔___ 6. ἀδελφός means **a brother**.

_____ 7. βλέπω means **I blow**.

☐ I practiced my flashcards today.

LET'S PRACTICE

Color the boxes yellow that have the same Greek words as the words in the big boxes.

ἀπόστολος	ἀπόδεκτος	ἀπόστολος
	ἀπόστολος	ἀποστάσιον

γινώσκω	γινώσκω	γογγύζω
	γαμέω	γινώσκω

βλέπω	βλέπω	βέλος
	βλέπω	βάπτω

Circle **yes** or **no**.

yes   no   1. γινώσκω means **I know**.

yes   no   2. ἄνθρωπος means **a church**.

yes   no   3. ἀδελφός means **a brother**.

yes   no   4. βλέπω means **I see**.

yes   no   5. γινώσκω means **I have**.

yes   no   6. βλέπω means **I burp**.

yes   no   7. ἀπόστολος means **a candle**.

☐ I practiced my flashcards today.

Greek Workbook - Level 2
Copyright © 1994 by Karen Mohs

LET'S PRACTICE

Draw lines from the Greek words to their meanings.

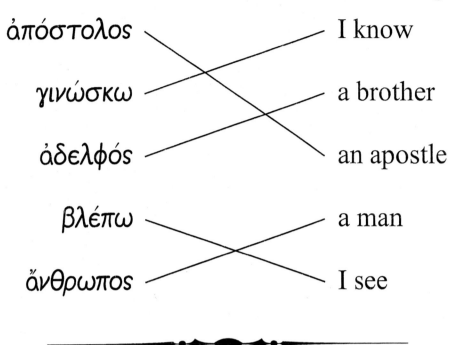

ἀπόστολος — I know

γινώσκω — a brother

ἀδελφός — an apostle

βλέπω — a man

ἄνθρωπος — I see

Fill in the blanks with the Greek words from the box.

| ἀπόστολος | γινώσκω | βλέπω |

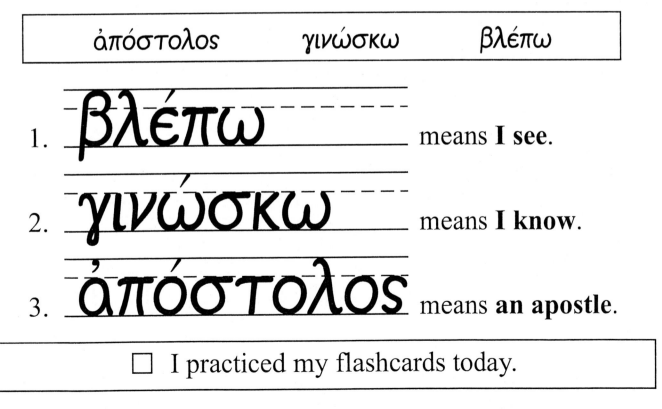

1. βλέπω means **I see**.

2. γινώσκω means **I know**.

3. ἀπόστολος means **an apostle**.

☐ I practiced my flashcards today.

LET'S PRACTICE

Draw lines from the sounds to their Greek words.

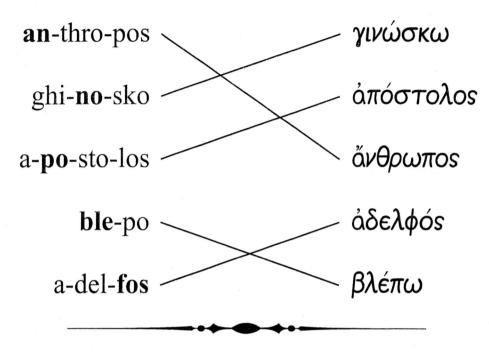

an-thro-pos   γινώσκω

ghi-no-sko   ἀπόστολος

a-po-sto-los   ἄνθρωπος

ble-po   ἀδελφός

a-del-fos   βλέπω

Circle the meanings of the Greek words.

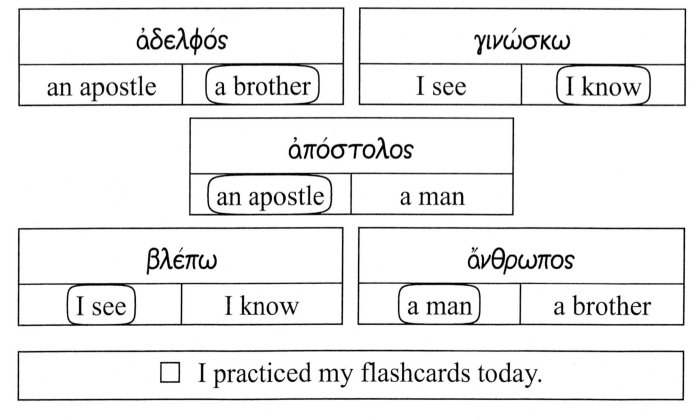

ἀδελφός	
an apostle	(a brother)

γινώσκω	
I see	(I know)

ἀπόστολος	
(an apostle)	a man

βλέπω	
(I see)	I know

ἄνθρωπος	
(a man)	a brother

☐ I practiced my flashcards today.

80

Greek Workbook - Level 2
Copyright © 1994 by Karen Mohs

LET'S PRACTICE

Circle the Greek words to match the meanings.

a brother
γινώσκω
βλέπω
ἄνθρωπος
(ἀδελφός)

an apostle
βλέπω
(ἀπόστολος)
ἀδελφός
ἄνθρωπος

I know
βλέπω
ἄνθρωπος
(γινώσκω)
ἀπόστολος

a man
(ἄνθρωπος)
γινώσκω
ἀπόστολος
ἀδελφός

I see
ἀπόστολος
ἀδελφός
(βλέπω)
γινώσκω

Write the Greek words.

I know   *γινώσκω*

an apostle   *ἀπόστολος*

a brother   *ἀδελφός*

I see   *βλέπω*

☐ I practiced my flashcards today.

LET'S PRACTICE

Write the Greek words.

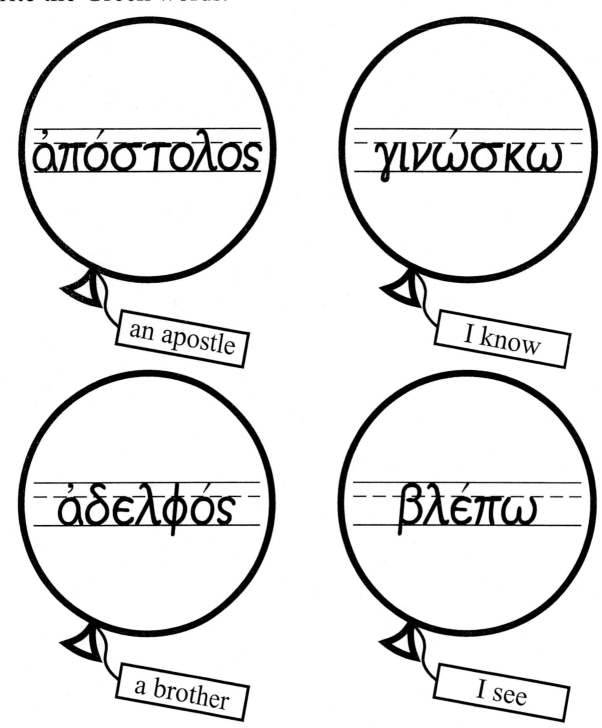

ἀπόστολος

an apostle

γινώσκω

I know

ἀδελφός

a brother

βλέπω

I see

☐ I practiced my flashcards today.

καί

means

and

It sounds like **kahee**.

Circle the Greek words that mean **and**.

καίω   κατά   καί
καί   καλός   κατά
κατά   καί   καίω
καλός   καίω   καλός

☐ I practiced my flashcards today. (Add the new card.)

More Practice
with
καί

Write the Greek word that means **and**.

καί   καί

καί   καί

καί   καί

καί   καί

καί   καί

καί   καί

καί   καί

☐ I practiced my flashcards today.

LET'S PRACTICE

Circle **yes** or **no**.

yes	(no)	1. καί means **why**.
(yes)	no	2. ἀπόστολος means **an apostle**.
(yes)	no	3. καί means **and**.
(yes)	no	4. γινώσκω means **I know**.
yes	(no)	5. βλέπω means **I sing**.
(yes)	no	6. ἄνθρωπος means **a man**.
yes	(no)	7. ἀδελφός means **a star**.

———◆•●•◆———

Write the meanings of the Greek words.

γινώσκω	I know
καί	and
ἀδελφός	a brother
ἄνθρωπος	a man
ἀπόστολος	an apostle
βλέπω	I see

☐ I practiced my flashcards today.

LET'S PRACTICE

Write the Greek words to match the sounds.

ghi-**no**-sko   γινώσκω

kahee   καί

a-**po**-sto-los   ἀπόστολος

ble-po   βλέπω

Color the boxes orange that have the same Greek words as the words in the big boxes.

γινώσκω	γογγύζω	γινώσκω
	γινώσκω	γίνομαι

καί	καί	καίω
	κατά	καί

βλέπω	βλέπω	βέλος
	βλέπω	βάπτω

☐ I practiced my flashcards today.

LET'S PRACTICE

Circle the Greek words to match the meanings.

I know	and	an apostle
(γινώσκω) βλέπω ἀπόστολος ἄνθρωπος	ἀπόστολος (καί) ἀδελφός γινώσκω	βλέπω (ἀπόστολος) ἀδελφός καί
a man	**I see**	**a brother**
ἀδελφός γινώσκω βλέπω (ἄνθρωπος)	(βλέπω) ἀδελφός καί ἄνθρωπος	ἄνθρωπος (ἀδελφός) γινώσκω ἀπόστολος

Connect the Greek words to their meanings in the ovals.

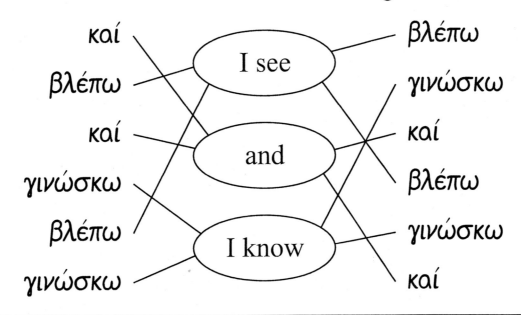

☐ I practiced my flashcards today.

LET'S PRACTICE

Circle the meanings of the Greek words.

βλέπω	
(I see)	and

ἀπόστολος	
a man	(an apostle)

ἄνθρωπος	
a brother	(a man)

καί	
a man	(and)

γινώσκω	
(I know)	I see

ἀδελφός	
an apostle	(a brother)

Check the blank if the sentence is true.

_____ 1. ἀδελφός means **a song**.

___✓___ 2. βλέπω means **I see**.

_____ 3. ἀπόστολος means **an owl**.

___✓___ 4. καί means **and**.

___✓___ 5. ἄνθρωπος means **a man**.

_____ 6. γινώσκω means **I scratch**.

_____ 7. καί means **often**.

☐ I practiced my flashcards today.

LET'S PRACTICE

Draw lines from the sounds to their Greek words.

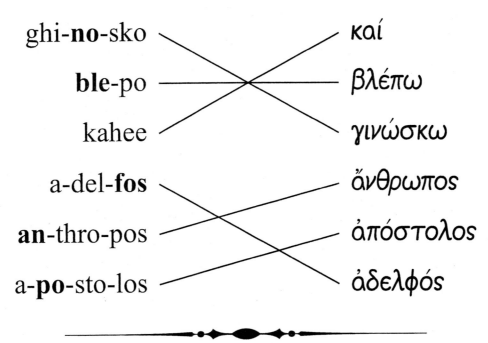

ghi-**no**-sko   καί

ble-po   βλέπω

kahee   γινώσκω

a-del-**fos**   ἄνθρωπος

an-thro-pos   ἀπόστολος

a-**po**-sto-los   ἀδελφός

———— ◆━●━◆ ————

Fill in the missing letters. Then write what the words mean.

κα_ί_

It means _and_ _____

γιν_ώ_σ_κ_ω

It means _I know_ _____

βλ_έ_π_ω_

It means _I see_ _____

☐ I practiced my flashcards today.

LET'S PRACTICE

Circle the Greek words to match the meanings.

I know	γινώσκω	ἀδελφός
	βλέπω	καί

and	βλέπω	ἀπόστολος
	καί	ἄνθρωπος

a brother	γινώσκω	ἄνθρωπος
	ἀπόστολος	ἀδελφός

———◆◆◆———

Write the Greek words.

and   καί

an apostle   ἀπόστολος

I know   γινώσκω

I see   βλέπω

☐ I practiced my flashcards today.

LET'S PRACTICE

Fill in the blanks with the Greek words from the box.

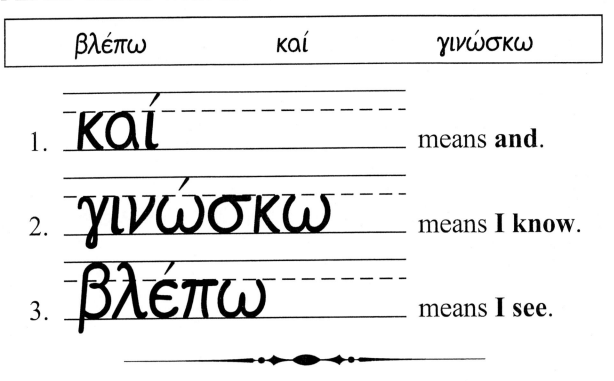

| βλέπω | καί | γινώσκω |

1. __καί_____ means **and**.

2. __γινώσκω_____ means **I know**.

3. __βλέπω_____ means **I see**.

───── ◆·◆·●·◆·◆ ─────

Draw lines from the Greek words to their meanings.

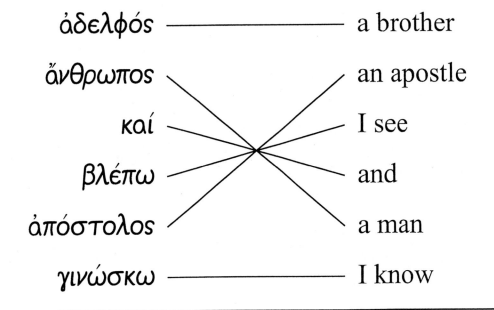

ἀδελφός ———————— a brother

ἄνθρωπος — an apostle

καί — I see

βλέπω — and

ἀπόστολος — a man

γινώσκω ———————— I know

☐ I practiced my flashcards today.

LET'S PRACTICE

Color the tags purple if the words inside mean the same.

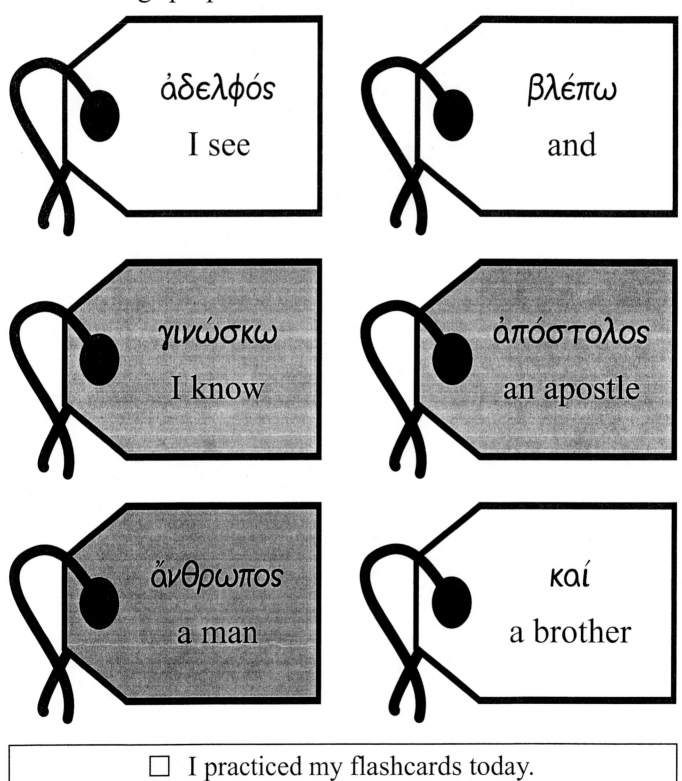

ἀδελφός

I see

βλέπω

and

γινώσκω

I know

ἀπόστολος

an apostle

ἄνθρωπος

a man

καί

a brother

☐ I practiced my flashcards today.

δοῦλος

means

a slave, a servant

It sounds like **doo**-los.

Circle the Greek words that mean **a slave**.

(δοῦλος)	δόλος	δῆλος
δῆμος	δῆλος	δόλος
δόλος	δῆμος	(δοῦλος)
δῆλος	(δοῦλος)	δῆμος

☐ I practiced my flashcards today. (Add the new card.)

More Practice
with
δοῦλος

Write the Greek word that means **a servant**.

δοῦλος   δοῦλος

δοῦλος   δοῦλος

δοῦλος   δοῦλος

δοῦλος   δοῦλος

δοῦλος   δοῦλος

δοῦλος   δοῦλος

δοῦλος   δοῦλος

☐ I practiced my flashcards today.

LET'S PRACTICE

Fill in the missing letters. Then write what the words mean.

γι_νώ_σκω

It means I know _____

_καί

It means and _____

δο_ῦλο_ς

It means a slave, a servant _____

———◆·◆·◆·◆———

Connect the Greek words to their meanings in the ovals.

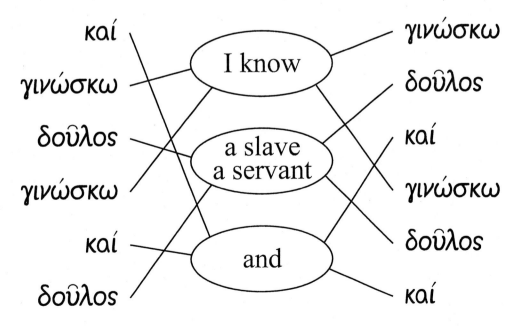

☐ I practiced my flashcards today.

LET'S PRACTICE

Write the Greek words to match the sounds.

doo-los   δοῦλος

ble-po   βλέπω

kahee   καί

ghi-**no**-sko   γινώσκω

Circle **yes** or **no**.

yes [no]   1. ἄνθρωπος means **a street**.

[yes] no   2. βλέπω means **I see**.

[yes] no   3. δοῦλος means **a slave**.

yes [no]   4. καί means **able**.

yes [no]   5. γινώσκω means **I need**.

[yes] no   6. ἀδελφός means **a brother**.

yes [no]   7. ἀπόστολος means **an apple**.

☐ I practiced my flashcards today.

96

Copyright © 1994 by Karen Mohs

LET'S PRACTICE

Write the meanings of the Greek words.

ἀδελφός	a brother
ἄνθρωπος	a man
ἀπόστολος	an apostle
γινώσκω	I know
καί	and
βλέπω	I see
δοῦλος	a slave, a servant

———— ◆•◆•◆ ————

Circle the Greek words to match the meanings.

and	βλέπω	ἀπόστολος
	(καί)	δοῦλος

an apostle	γινώσκω	ἀδελφός
	(ἀπόστολος)	καί

a servant	(δοῦλος)	γινώσκω
	βλέπω	ἄνθρωπος

☐ I practiced my flashcards today.

LET'S PRACTICE

Write the Greek words.

I know   *γινώσκω*

a slave   *δοῦλος*

I see   *βλέπω*

and   *καί*

Circle the Greek words to match the meanings.

an apostle	I see	and
γινώσκω ⟨ἀπόστολος⟩ ἀδελφός καί	ἀπόστολος γινώσκω ⟨βλέπω⟩ δοῦλος	δοῦλος ⟨καί⟩ βλέπω ἀδελφός
a servant	**a brother**	**I know**
⟨δοῦλος⟩ καί βλέπω ἄνθρωπος	ἀπόστολος ἄνθρωπος βλέπω ⟨ἀδελφός⟩	⟨γινώσκω⟩ ἄνθρωπος ἀδελφός δοῦλος

☐ I practiced my flashcards today.

Greek Workbook - Level 2
Copyright © 1994 by Karen Mohs

LET'S PRACTICE

Draw lines from the Greek words to their meanings.

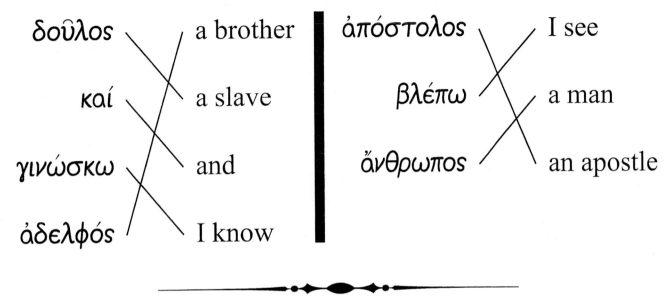

δοῦλος — a brother
καί — a slave
γινώσκω — and
ἀδελφός — I know

ἀπόστολος — I see
βλέπω — a man
ἄνθρωπος — an apostle

Color the boxes brown that have the same Greek words as the words in the big boxes.

καί	καίω	καί
	καί	κατά

δοῦλος	δοῦλος	δοῦλος
	δόλος	δῆλος

γινώσκω	γογγύζω	γίνομαι
	γινώσκω	γινώσκω

☐ I practiced my flashcards today.

LET'S PRACTICE

Fill in the blanks with the Greek words from the box.

καί	ἄνθρωπος	δοῦλος

1. __δοῦλος__ means **a servant**.

2. __ἄνθρωπος__ means **a man**.

3. __καί__ means **and**.

———◆◆◆———

Circle the meanings of the Greek words.

γινώσκω	
(I know)	I see

βλέπω	
I know	(I see)

ἀδελφός	
(a brother)	a slave

δοῦλος	
and	(a slave)

καί	
I see	(and)

ἀπόστολος	
a man	(an apostle)

☐ I practiced my flashcards today.

Greek Workbook - Level 2
Copyright © 1994 by Karen Mohs

LET'S PRACTICE

Draw lines from the sounds to their Greek words.

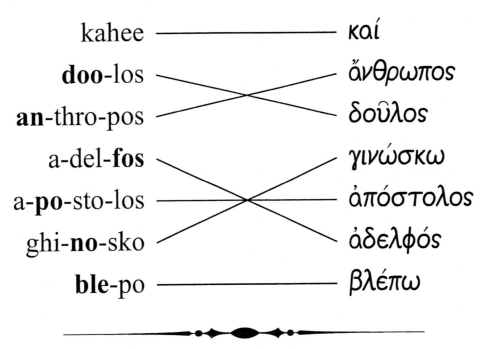

kahee	καί
doo-los	ἄνθρωπος
an-thro-pos	δοῦλος
a-del-**fos**	γινώσκω
a-**po**-sto-los	ἀπόστολος
ghi-**no**-sko	ἀδελφός
ble-po	βλέπω

Check the blank if the sentence is true.

_____ 1. γινώσκω means **I want**.

_____ 2. ἄνθρωπος means **a cave**.

✓ 3. καί means **and**.

_____ 4. δοῦλος means **a master**.

_____ 5. ἀπόστολος means **a man**.

✓ 6. βλέπω means **I see**.

✓ 7. ἀδελφός means **a brother**.

☐ I practiced my flashcards today.

LET'S PRACTICE

Fill the hourglasses with the correct Greek words.

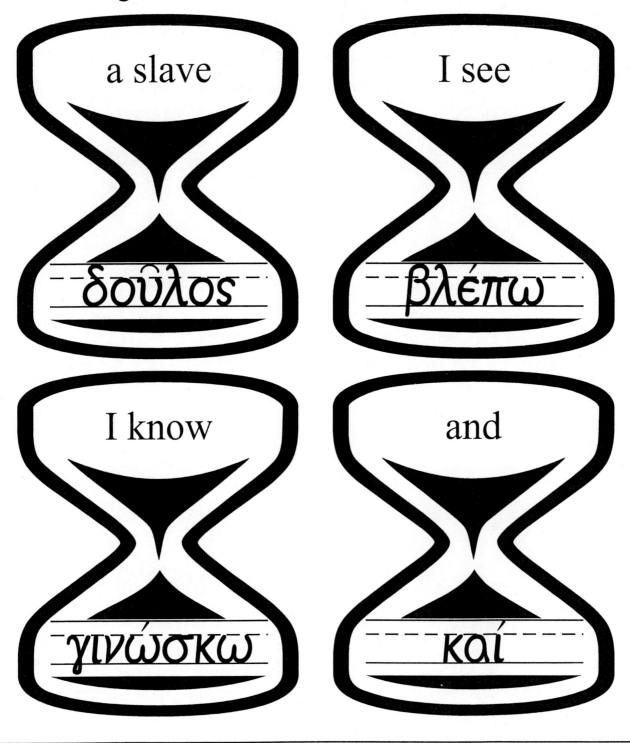

a slave

δοῦλος

I see

βλέπω

I know

γινώσκω

and

καί

☐ I practiced my flashcards today.

λόγος

means

a word

It sounds like **lo**-gos.

Circle the Greek words that mean **a word**.

λύκος	(λόγος)	λεῖος
(λόγος)	λύκος	λύχνος
λεῖος	λύχνος	(λόγος)
λύχνος	λεῖος	λύκος

☐ I practiced my flashcards today. (Add the new card.)

More Practice
with
λόγος

Write the Greek word that means **a word**.

λόγος   λόγος

λόγος   λόγος

λόγος   λόγος

λόγος   λόγος

λόγος   λόγος

λόγος   λόγος

λόγος   λόγος

☐ I practiced my flashcards today.

LET'S PRACTICE

Circle the Greek words to match the meanings.

a word	a man	I know
δοῦλος (λόγος) ἀδελφός βλέπω	(ἄνθρωπος) καί ἀπόστολος λόγος	βλέπω ἀδελφός (γινώσκω) δοῦλος
and	**a servant**	**I see**
λόγος ἄνθρωπος βλέπω (καί)	ἀδελφός ἀπόστολος λόγος (δοῦλος)	γινώσκω (βλέπω) καί ἄνθρωπος

———————◆•◆———————

Fill in the missing letters. Then write what the words mean.

λόγος

It means <u>a word</u>

δοῦλος

It means <u>a slave, a servant</u>

καί

It means <u>and</u>

☐ I practiced my flashcards today.

LET'S PRACTICE

Circle the Greek words to match the meanings.

a word	καί	λόγος
	γινώσκω	ἀπόστολος

a slave	ἀδελφός	καί
	δοῦλος	ἄνθρωπος

I see	λόγος	βλέπω
	δοῦλος	γινώσκω

———◆•❖•◆———

Draw lines from the Greek words to their meanings.

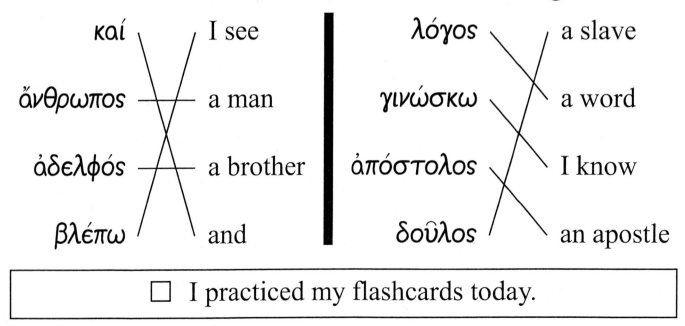

καί	I see	λόγος	a slave
ἄνθρωπος	a man	γινώσκω	a word
ἀδελφός	a brother	ἀπόστολος	I know
βλέπω	and	δοῦλος	an apostle

☐ I practiced my flashcards today.

LET'S PRACTICE

Connect the Greek words to their meanings in the ovals.

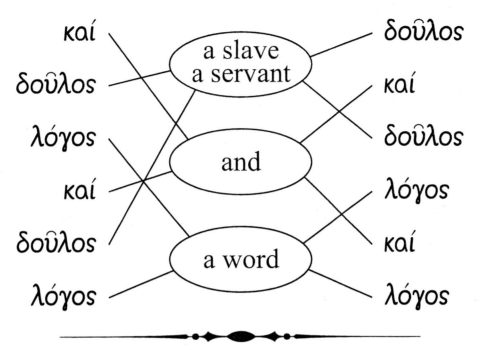

Write the meanings of the Greek words.

λόγος	a word
γινώσκω	I know
βλέπω	I see
ἀδελφός	a brother
δοῦλος	a slave, a servant
ἀπόστολος	an apostle
καί	and

☐ I practiced my flashcards today.

LET'S PRACTICE

Check the blank if the sentence is true.

    _____   1. καί means **against**.

    ✓   2. γινώσκω means **I know**.

    ✓   3. ἀπόστολος means **an apostle**.

    _____   4. βλέπω means **I cook**.

    ✓   5. δοῦλος means **a slave**.

    _____   6. ἀδελφός means **a nephew**.

    _____   7. λόγος means **a fireplace**.

Write the Greek words to match the sounds.

kahee   καί

lo-gos   λόγος

ghi-**no**-sko   γινώσκω

doo-los   δοῦλος

☐ I practiced my flashcards today.

Greek Workbook - Level 2
Copyright © 1994 by Karen Mohs

LET'S PRACTICE

Color the boxes red that have the same Greek words as the words in the big boxes.

καί	καί	καλός
	καίω	καί

λόγος	λόγος	λεῖος
	λόγος	λύκος

δοῦλος	δοῦλος	δῆλος
	δόλος	δοῦλος

———————◆———————

Fill in the blanks with the Greek words from the box.

ἀδελφός	λόγος	βλέπω

1. __λόγος__ means **a word**.

2. __βλέπω__ means **I see**.

3. __ἀδελφός__ means **a brother**.

☐ I practiced my flashcards today.

LET'S PRACTICE

Circle the meanings of the Greek words.

δοῦλος	
(a slave)	a word

καί	
a brother	(and)

λόγος	
a man	(a word)

γινώσκω	
I see	(I know)

ἀπόστολος	
(an apostle)	a man

βλέπω	
(I see)	I know

———— ◆ ━ ● ━ ◆ ————

Write the Greek words.

a slave ___δοῦλος___

I see ___βλέπω___

a word ___λόγος___

I know ___γινώσκω___

☐ I practiced my flashcards today.

LET'S PRACTICE

Draw lines from the sounds to their Greek words.

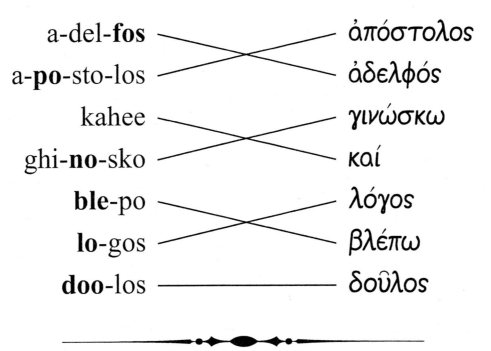

a-del-**fos**   ἀπόστολος

a-**po**-sto-los   ἀδελφός

kahee   γινώσκω

ghi-**no**-sko   καί

ble-po   λόγος

lo-gos   βλέπω

doo-los   δοῦλος

Circle **yes** or **no**.

yes   no   1. ἀπόστολος means **an apostle**.

yes   no   2. γινώσκω means **I know**.

yes   no   3. λόγος means **a word**.

yes   no   4. δοῦλος means **a duty**.

yes   no   5. καί means **and**.

yes   no   6. βλέπω means **I love**.

yes   no   7. ἀδελφός means **an uncle**.

☐ I practiced my flashcards today.

LET'S PRACTICE

Color the glasses blue if the words inside mean the same.

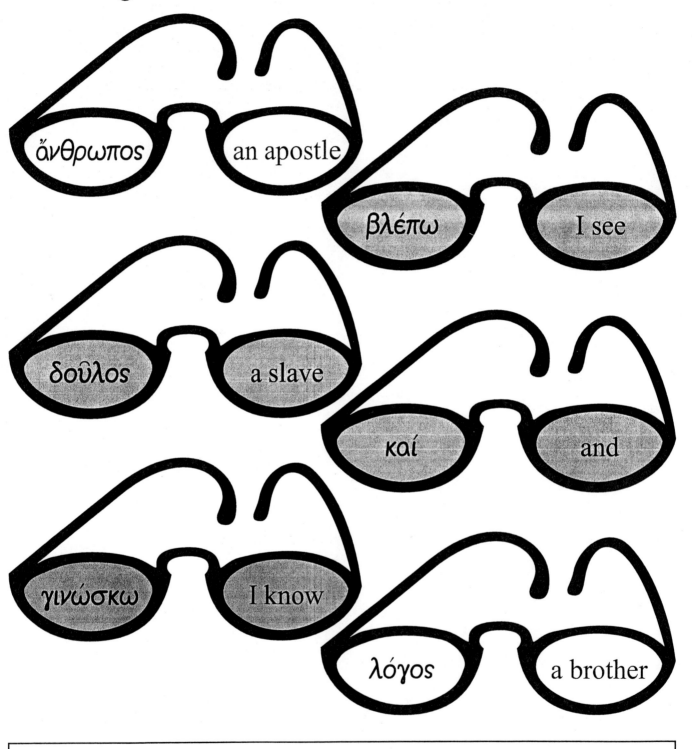

ἄνθρωπος — an apostle

βλέπω — I see

δοῦλος — a slave

καί — and

γινώσκω — I know

λόγος — a brother

☐ I practiced my flashcards today.

means

I write

It sounds like **gra**-fo.

Circle the Greek words that mean **I write**.

γελάω   γέμω   γινώσκω
γέμω   γελάω   γράφω
γράφω   γινώσκω   γελάω
γινώσκω   γράφω   γέμω

☐ I practiced my flashcards today. (Add the new card.)

More Practice
with
γράφω

Write the Greek word that means **I write**.

γράφω   γράφω

γράφω   γράφω

γράφω   γράφω

γράφω   γράφω

γράφω   γράφω

γράφω   γράφω

γράφω   γράφω

☐ I practiced my flashcards today.

Greek Workbook - Level 2
Copyright © 1994 by Karen Mohs

LET'S PRACTICE

Write the meanings of the Greek words.

καί   <u>and</u>

δοῦλος   <u>a slave, a servant</u>

λόγος   <u>a word</u>

βλέπω   <u>I see</u>

ἀπόστολος   <u>an apostle</u>

γράφω   <u>I write</u>

γινώσκω   <u>I know</u>

Draw lines from the Greek words to their meanings.

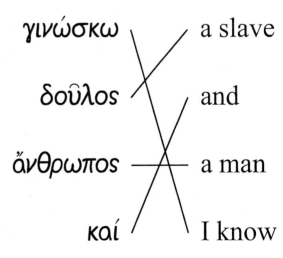

☐ I practiced my flashcards today.

LET'S PRACTICE

Write the Greek words to match the sounds.

gra-fo γράφω

doo-los δοῦλος

kahee καί

lo-gos λόγος

Check the blank if the sentence is true.

_____ ✔ _____ 1. λόγος means **a word**.

_____ 2. δοῦλος means **I cry**.

_____ ✔ _____ 3. καί means **and**.

_____ ✔ _____ 4. βλέπω means **I see**.

_____ 5. ἀπόστολος means **a statue**.

_____ 6. γράφω means **I laugh**.

_____ 7. γινώσκω means **I sneeze**.

☐ I practiced my flashcards today.

116

LET'S PRACTICE

Color the boxes green that have the same Greek words as the words in the big boxes.

δοῦλος	δῆλος	δοῦλος
	δόλος	δοῦλος

γράφω	γέμω	γελάω
	γράφω	γράφω

λόγος	λύκος	λόγος
	λόγος	λεῖος

Circle **yes** or **no**.

(yes)	no	1. βλέπω means **I see**.
yes	(no)	2. καί means **otherwise**.
(yes)	no	3. γράφω means **I write**.
yes	(no)	4. λόγος means **a log**.
yes	(no)	5. ἀπόστολος means **an award**.
yes	(no)	6. γινώσκω means **I give**.
(yes)	no	7. δοῦλος means **a servant**.

☐ I practiced my flashcards today.

LET'S PRACTICE

Fill in the blanks with the Greek words from the box.

γινώσκω	γράφω	βλέπω

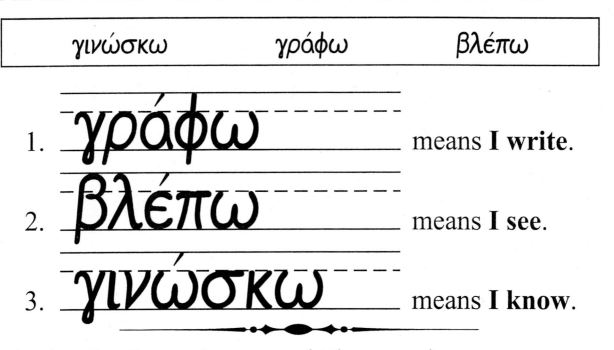

1. γράφω _____ means **I write**.

2. βλέπω _____ means **I see**.

3. γινώσκω _____ means **I know**.

Circle the Greek words to match the meanings.

a servant	an apostle	a word
(δοῦλος) ἄνθρωπος βλέπω γράφω	ἄνθρωπος ἀδελφός (ἀπόστολος) δοῦλος	ἀπόστολος δοῦλος ἀδελφός (λόγος)
I write	**a brother**	**and**
(γράφω) βλέπω καί γινώσκω	λόγος γινώσκω (ἀδελφός) ἄνθρωπος	γράφω βλέπω λόγος (καί)

☐ I practiced my flashcards today.

Greek Workbook - Level 2
Copyright © 1994 by Karen Mohs

LET'S PRACTICE

Connect the Greek words to their meanings in the ovals.

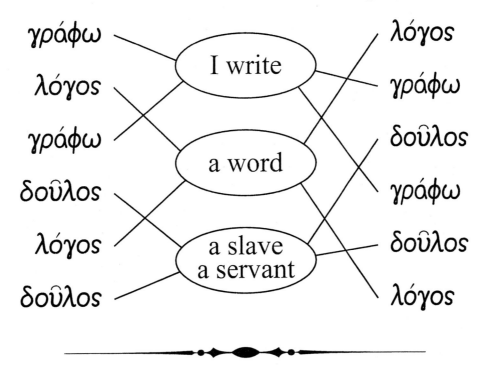

Draw lines from the sounds to their Greek words.

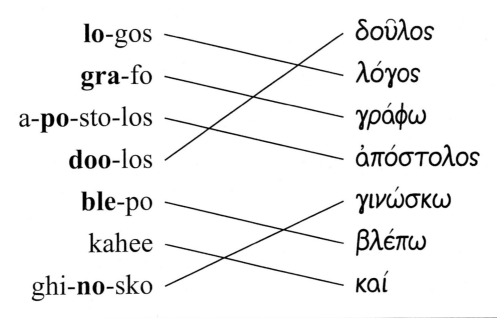

□ I practiced my flashcards today.

LET'S PRACTICE

Fill in the missing letters. Then write what the words mean.

δοῦλος

It means <u>a slave, a servant</u>

λόγος

It means <u>a word</u>

γράφω

It means <u>I write</u>

---◆—●—◆---

Circle the meanings of the Greek words.

λόγος	
(a word)	and

γινώσκω	
I write	(I know)

καί	
a slave	(and)

γράφω	
I see	(I write)

βλέπω	
(I see)	I know

δοῦλος	
(a slave)	a word

☐ I practiced my flashcards today.

120

LET'S PRACTICE

Write the Greek words.

I write _γράφω_

a slave _δοῦλος_

and _καί_

a word _λόγος_

———— ·•·<•>•·• ————

Circle the Greek words to match the meanings.

I know	γράφω	(γινώσκω)
	λόγος	καί

I write	δοῦλος	ἄνθρωπος
	βλέπω	(γράφω)

a word	δοῦλος	(λόγος)
	ἀδελφός	ἀπόστολος

☐ I practiced my flashcards today.

LET'S PRACTICE

Help the farmer find the Greek words.

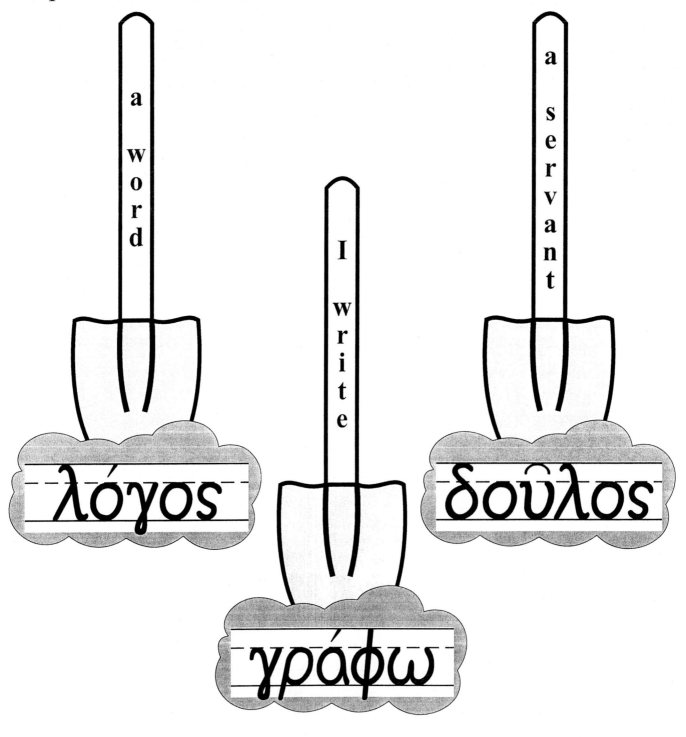

a
w
o
r
d

λόγος

I
w
r
i
t
e

γράφω

a
s
e
r
v
a
n
t

δοῦλος

☐ I practiced my flashcards today.

υἱός

means

a son

It sounds like hwee-**os**.

Circle the Greek words that mean **a son**.

ⓥἱός   ὑγρός   ὑπό
ὑγρός   ὑπό   ὕμνος
ὕμνος   ⓥἱός   ὑγρός
ὑπό   ὕμνος   ⓥἱός

☐ I practiced my flashcards today. (Add the new card.)

More Practice
with
υἱός

Write the Greek word that means **a son**.

υἱός   υἱός

υἱός   υἱός

υἱός   υἱός

υἱός   υἱός

υἱός   υἱός

υἱός   υἱός

υἱός   υἱός

☐ I practiced my flashcards today.

LET'S PRACTICE

Draw lines from the Greek words to their meanings.

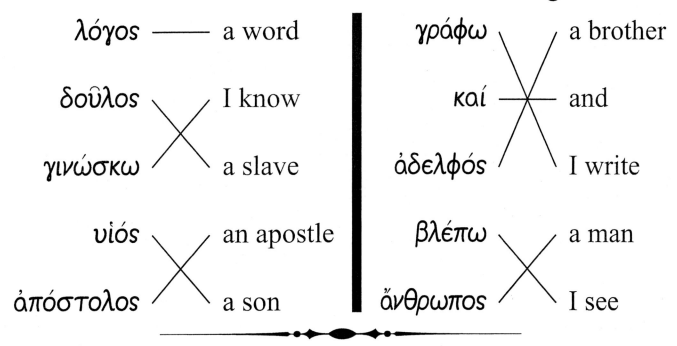

λόγος	—— a word	γράφω	a brother
δοῦλος	I know	καί	and
γινώσκω	a slave	ἀδελφός	I write
υἱός	an apostle	βλέπω	a man
ἀπόστολος	a son	ἄνθρωπος	I see

Color the boxes pink that have the same Greek words as the words in the big boxes.

υἱός	ὕμνος	ὑπό
	υἱός	υἱός

γράφω	γράφω	γέμω
	γελάω	γράφω

λόγος	λόγος	λύκος
	λόγος	λύχνος

☐ I practiced my flashcards today.

LET'S PRACTICE

Fill in the missing letters. Then write what the words mean.

υἱός

It means a son _____

γράφω

It means I write _____

λόγος

It means a word _____

---------------◆-------------

Write the meanings of the Greek words.

δοῦλος	a slave, a servant
υἱός	a son
καί	and
γράφω	I write
βλέπω	I see
γινώσκω	I know
λόγος	a word

☐ I practiced my flashcards today.

LET'S PRACTICE

Circle **yes** or **no**.

(yes)	no	1. υἱός means **a son**.
yes	(no)	2. δοῦλος means **a pineapple**.
(yes)	no	3. γινώσκω means **I know**.
yes	(no)	4. γράφω means **I grumble**.
yes	(no)	5. βλέπω means **I jump**.
(yes)	no	6. καί means **and**.
(yes)	no	7. λόγος means **a word**.

———— ◆ ————

Write the Greek words to match the sounds.

lo-gos   λόγος

hwee-**os**   υἱός

gra-fo   γράφω

doo-los   δοῦλος

☐ I practiced my flashcards today.

LET'S PRACTICE

Circle the meanings of the Greek words.

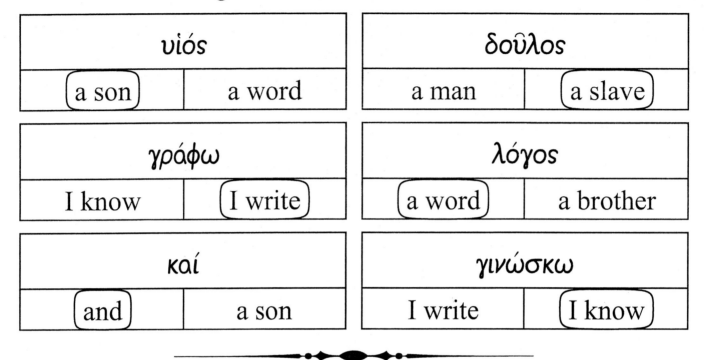

υἱός	
(a son)	a word

δοῦλος	
a man	(a slave)

γράφω	
I know	(I write)

λόγος	
(a word)	a brother

καί	
(and)	a son

γινώσκω	
I write	(I know)

Connect the Greek words to their meanings in the ovals.

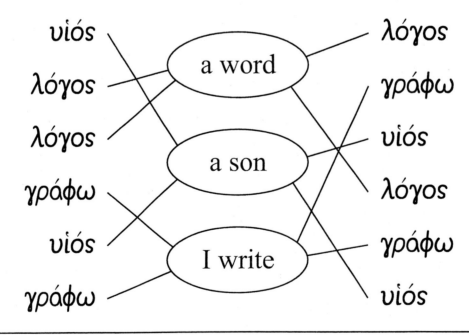

υἱός

λόγος   λόγος

λόγος

a word   γράφω

γράφω   υἱός

a son   λόγος

υἱός

γράφω   I write

υἱός

γράφω   υἱός

☐ I practiced my flashcards today.

LET'S PRACTICE

Check the blank if the sentence is true.

   ✔   1. γράφω means **I write**.

   ✔   2. γινώσκω means **I know**.

   ✔   3. δοῦλος means **a servant**.

         4. υἱός means **a rainbow**.

         5. λόγος means **a tree**.

         6. καί means **but**.

         7. βλέπω means **I cough**.

Write the Greek words.

a word   λόγος

I write   γράφω

a son   υἱός

a slave   δοῦλος

☐ I practiced my flashcards today.

LET'S PRACTICE

Draw lines from the sounds to their Greek words.

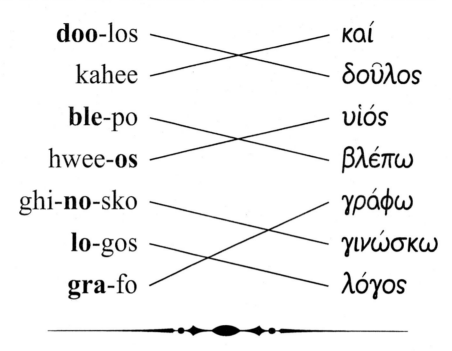

doo-los	καί
kahee	δοῦλος
ble-po	υἱός
hwee-**os**	βλέπω
ghi-**no**-sko	γράφω
lo-gos	γινώσκω
gra-fo	λόγος

———————◆●◆———————

Circle the Greek words to match the meanings.

and	λόγος	υἱός
	⟨καί⟩	γράφω

a son	⟨υἱός⟩	δοῦλος
	ἄνθρωπος	ἀπόστολος

I write	γινώσκω	⟨γράφω⟩
	ἀδελφός	βλέπω

☐ I practiced my flashcards today.

LET'S PRACTICE

Circle the Greek words to match the meanings.

I know	a son	a word
γράφω βλέπω (γινώσκω) λόγος	ἀπόστολος δοῦλος (υἱός) ἀδελφός	ἀδελφός καί δοῦλος (λόγος)
I write	**I see**	**a man**
γινώσκω υἱός (γράφω) βλέπω	(βλέπω) γινώσκω ἀδελφός γράφω	καί ἀδελφός λόγος (ἄνθρωπος)

───────── ◆ • ◆ • ◆ ─────────

Fill in the blanks with the Greek words from the box.

δοῦλος	υἱός	ἀπόστολος

1. __ἀπόστολος__ means **an apostle.**

2. __δοῦλος__ means **a servant.**

3. __υἱός__ means **a son.**

☐ I practiced my flashcards today.

LET'S PRACTICE

Color the frames orange if the words inside mean the same.

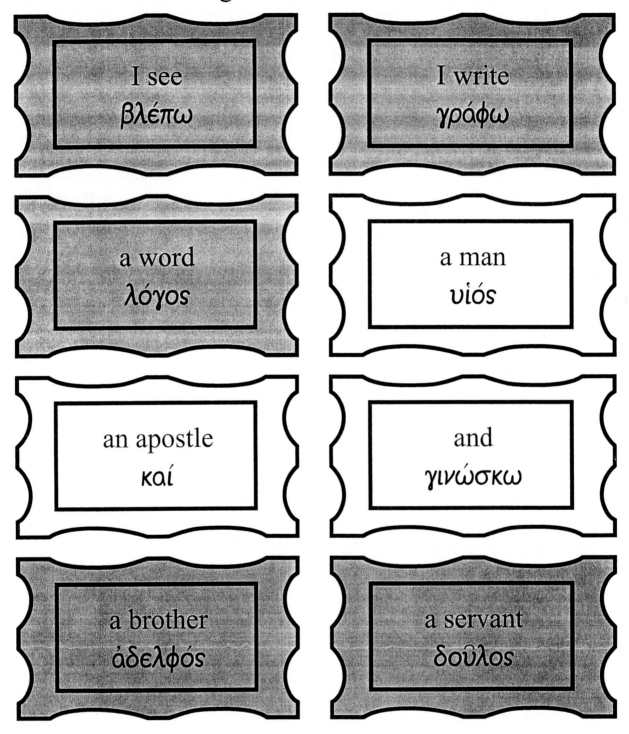

☐ I practiced my flashcards today.

means

I teach

It sounds like di-**da**-sko.

Circle the Greek words that mean **I teach**.

διεγείρω   (διδάσκω)   διπλόος
δίδωμι   διπλόος   διεγείρω
διπλόος   δίδωμι   (διδάσκω)
(διδάσκω)   διεγείρω   δίδωμι

☐   I practiced my flashcards today. (Add the new card.)

More Practice
with
διδάσκω

Write the Greek word that means **I teach**.

διδάσκω   διδάσκω

διδάσκω   διδάσκω

διδάσκω   διδάσκω

διδάσκω   διδάσκω

διδάσκω   διδάσκω

διδάσκω   διδάσκω

διδάσκω   διδάσκω

☐ I practiced my flashcards today.

LET'S PRACTICE

Circle the meanings of the Greek words.

γράφω	
I see	(I write)

λόγος	
a man	(a word)

δοῦλος	
(a slave)	a son

διδάσκω	
(I teach)	I know

γινώσκω	
I write	(I know)

υἱός	
(a son)	a slave

———— ◆●◆ ————

Write the meanings of the Greek words.

λόγος	a word
διδάσκω	I teach
γινώσκω	I know
δοῦλος	a slave, a servant
καί	and
υἱός	a son
γράφω	I write

☐ I practiced my flashcards today.

LET'S PRACTICE

Connect the Greek words to their meanings in the ovals.

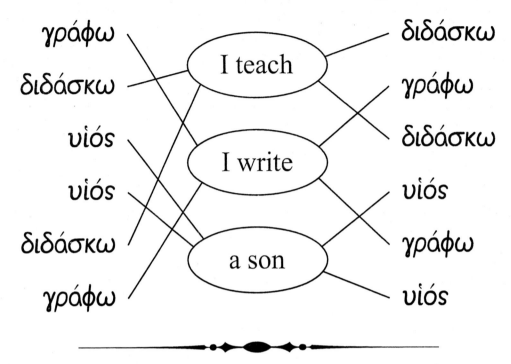

γράφω

διδάσκω

υἱός

υἱός

διδάσκω

γράφω

I teach

I write

a son

διδάσκω

γράφω

διδάσκω

υἱός

γράφω

υἱός

Fill in the missing letters. Then write what the words mean.

γρά<u>φ</u><u>ω</u>

It means <u>I write</u>

δι<u>δ</u>ά<u>σ</u>κ<u>ω</u>

It means <u>I teach</u>

<u>υ</u>ἱό<u>s</u>

It means <u>a son</u>

☐ I practiced my flashcards today.

LET'S PRACTICE

Circle the Greek words to match the meanings.

a servant	I know	I see
(δοῦλος)	γράφω	διδάσκω
ἀδελφός	διδάσκω	(βλέπω)
λόγος	βλέπω	γινώσκω
υἱός	(γινώσκω)	γράφω

a son	I teach	I write
λόγος	γινώσκω	(γράφω)
ἀδελφός	(διδάσκω)	γινώσκω
δοῦλος	γράφω	καί
(υἱός)	βλέπω	διδάσκω

Circle **yes** or **no**.

(yes) no   1. γράφω means **I write**.

yes (no)   2. λόγος means **a chart**.

yes (no)   3. καί means **while**.

(yes) no   4. διδάσκω means **I teach**.

yes (no)   5. γινώσκω means **I grow**.

(yes) no   6. δοῦλος means **a slave**.

yes (no)   7. υἱός means **a swing**.

□ I practiced my flashcards today.

LET'S PRACTICE

Write the Greek words to match the sounds.

gra-fo *γράφω*

lo-gos *λόγος*

di-**da**-sko *διδάσκω*

hwee-**os** *υἱός*

———— ◆●◆ ————

Circle the Greek words to match the meanings.

I teach	γινώσκω	(διδάσκω)
	γράφω	βλέπω

a servant	ἄνθρωπος	ἀπόστολος
	(δοῦλος)	διδάσκω

a son	(υἱός)	λόγος
	καί	ἀδελφός

☐ I practiced my flashcards today.

LET'S PRACTICE

Fill in the blanks with the Greek words from the box.

γράφω	διδάσκω	υἱός

1. __διδάσκω__ means **I teach**.

2. __υἱός__ means **a son**.

3. __γράφω__ means **I write**.

───── ◆ ━━ ◆ ─────

Draw lines from the Greek words to their meanings.

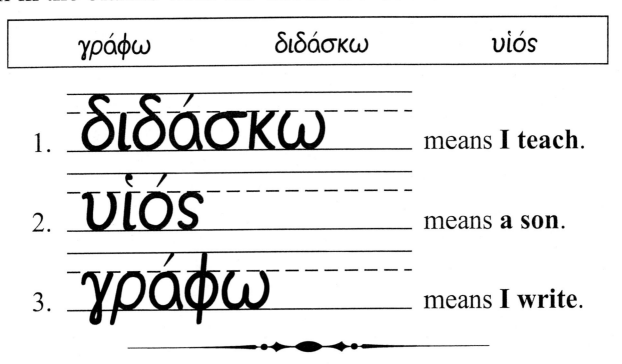

διδάσκω	a son
ἀδελφός	a brother
υἱός	I teach
καί	I see
γράφω	I write
βλέπω	and

ἄνθρωπος	a man
ἀπόστολος	a word
γινώσκω	I know
λόγος	an apostle
δοῦλος	a slave

☐ I practiced my flashcards today.

LET'S PRACTICE

Color the boxes purple that have the same Greek words as the words in the big boxes.

γράφω	γέμω	γράφω
	γράφω	γελάω

διδάσκω	διδάσκω	διπλόος
	διδάσκω	διεγείρω

υἱός	υἱός	ὕμνος
	ὑπό	υἱός

—◆—

Write the Greek words.

a son _υἱός_

a word _λόγος_

I write _γράφω_

I teach _διδάσκω_

☐ I practiced my flashcards today.

LET'S PRACTICE

Check the blank if the sentence is true.

 1. καί means **and**.

_____ 2. δοῦλος means **an ant**.

 3. υἱός means **a son**.

_____ 4. γινώσκω means **I search**.

 5. διδάσκω means **I teach**.

 6. λόγος means **a word**.

_____ 7. γράφω means **I stop**.

———————— ◆•●•◆ ————————

Draw lines from the sounds to their Greek words.

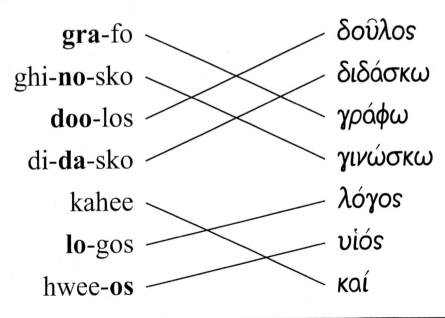

gra-fo	δοῦλος
ghi-**no**-sko	διδάσκω
doo-los	γράφω
di-**da**-sko	γινώσκω
kahee	λόγος
lo-gos	υἱός
hwee-**os**	καί

☐ I practiced my flashcards today.

LET'S PRACTICE

Write the Greek words on the pitchers.

I teach — διδάσκω

I write — γράφω

a word — λόγος

a son — υἱός

☐ I practiced my flashcards today.

LET'S PRACTICE

Write the Greek words.

I see   *βλέπω*

I teach   *διδάσκω*

a word   *λόγος*

a brother   *ἀδελφός*

I know   *γινώσκω*

a son   *υἱός*

a man   *ἄνθρωπος*

an apostle   *ἀπόστολος*

I write   *γράφω*

and   *καί*

a slave   *δοῦλος*

☐ I practiced my flashcards today.

APPENDIX

Glossaries

Greek - English

α

ἀγαπητός - beloved
ἁγιασμός - moral purity
ἀδελφός - a brother (43)
ἄδικος - unjust
ἄδολος - sincere
ἀθέμιτος - unlawful
ἄνθρωπος - a man (37)
ἄπιστος - unbelieving
ἀπόδεκτος - acceptable
ἀποστάσιον - desertion
ἀπόστολος - an apostle (53)

β

βάλλω - I throw
βάπτω - I baptize
βέλος - a dart
βλέπω - I see (63)

γ

γαμέω - I marry
γελάω - I laugh
γέμω - I am full
γίνομαι - I become
γινώσκω - I know (73)
γογγύζω - I mutter
γράφω - I write (113)

δ

δῆλος - clearly visible
δῆμος - a people
διδάσκω - I teach (133)
δίδωμι - I give
διεγείρω - I arouse
διπλόος - double
δόλος - fraud

δοῦλος - a slave, a servant (93)

κ

καί - and (83)
καίω - I kindle
καλός - beautiful
κατά - down from

λ

λεῖος - smooth
λόγος - a word (103)
λύκος - a wolf
λύχνος - a light

υ

ὑγρός - moist
υἱός - a son (123)
ὕμνος - a song
ὑπό - under

English - Greek

a

and - καί
apostle - ἀπόστολος

b

brother - ἀδελφός

k

know - γινώσκω

m

man - ἄνθρωπος

s

see - βλέπω
servant - δοῦλος
slave - δοῦλος
son - υἱός

t

teach - διδάσκω

w

word - λόγος
write - γράφω

Note: The number in parentheses indicates the page on which the vocabulary word is introduced.

146

APPENDIX

Greek Alphabet

Capital Letter	Small Letter	Name	Pronunciation	Capital Letter	Small Letter	Name	Pronunciation
A	α	alpha (**al**-fa)	**a** in *father*	N	ν	nu (noo)	**n** in *nice*
B	β	beta (**bay**-ta)	**b** in *bat*	Ξ	ξ	xi (ksee)	**x** in *box*
Γ	γ	gamma (**gam**-ma)	**g** in *God*	O	o	omicron (**ahm**-i-cron)	**o** in *obey**
Δ	δ	delta (**del**-ta)	**d** in *dog*	Π	π	pi (pie)	**p** in *pie*
E	ε	epsilon (**ep**-si-lon)	**e** in *get*	P	ρ	rho (row)	**r** in *row*
Z	ζ	zeta (**zay**-ta)	**dz** in *adze*	Σ	σ ς	sigma (**sig**-ma)	**s** in *sit*
H	η	eta (**ay**-ta)	**a** in *late*	T	τ	tau (tou)	**t** in *toy*
Θ	θ	theta (**thay**-ta)	**th** in *bath*	Y	υ	upsilon (**up**-si-lon)	**oo** in *good*
I	ι	iota (ee-**o**-ta)	**i** in *pit*	Φ	φ	phi (fee)	**f** in *fun*
K	κ	kappa (**kap**-pa)	**k** in *kite*	X	χ	chi (kee)	**ch** in *Ach*
Λ	λ	lambda (**lamb**-da)	**l** in *lamb*	Ψ	ψ	psi (psee)	**ps** in *lips*
M	μ	mu (moo)	**m** in *man*	Ω	ω	omega (o-**may**-ga)	**o** in *note**

*The o and the ω both have a long o sound, but the ω is held longer.

Vowels and Diphthongs

Short Vowels:

α	**a** in *father*
ε	**e** in *get*
o	**o** in *obey*
ι	**i** in *pit*
υ	**oo** in *good*

Long Vowels:

α	**a** in *father*, but held longer
η	**a** in *late*
ω	**o** in *note*
ι	**ee** in *feet*
υ	**oo** in *good*, but held longer

Most common Greek diphthongs:

αι	**ai** in *aisle*
ει	**a** in *fate* (same sound as η)
οι	**oi** in *oil*
αυ	**ow** in *cow*
ευ	**eu** in *feud*
ου	**oo** in *food*
υι	**uee** in *queen*

(Note: A diphthong combines two vowels into one syllable. For example, the **oi** in our English word **boil** is a diphthong.)

When an iota (ι) follows certain long vowels (α, η, ω), it is written below the letter instead of after it (ᾳ, ῃ, ῳ). This is called an **iota subscript**. These diphthongs sound the same as the long vowels alone.

APPENDIX

Flashcard Tips

1. Remember to practice flashcards daily.

2. Do not move ahead in the workbook if your student is struggling for mastery. Review the flashcards every day until your student is confident and ready to learn more.